Grumman F-14 "Tomcat"

by James Perry Stevenson

AERO PUBLISHERS, INC.

329 West Aviation Road, Fallbrook, CA 92028

Library of Congress Cataloging in Publication Data

Stevenson, James Perry.
  Grumman F-14 "Tomcat".

  (Aero series ; v. 25)
  Includes bibliographical references and index.
  1. Tomcat (Jet fighter plane) I. Title.
TL686.G78S74   623.74'64   75-7465
ISBN 0-8168-0592-X

Contents

To My Parents and Sandra

Foreword

In this book Mr. Stevenson has provided a significant service to the American citizen and taxpayer. A modern combat aircraft such as the F-14 is expensive and complex. The reasoning behind the requirement for such equipment deserves the thoughtful treatment given herein.

There has been much public discussion devoted to the F-14 before this book, but such discussion has focused almost exclusively on its cost. Mr. Stevenson has added balance to the picture and contributed to the sharpening of the reader's perspective by including why we need the capabilities of a weapons system like the F-14 and how well the F-14 does in meeting the operational challenges that define its requirement.

For the pure aviation buff and/or technical reader, this book offers some depth of coverage of the quite remarkable and versatile capabilities of the *Tomcat/Phoenix* combination, covering the spectrum from long range search and missile kill of bomber or cruise missile type targets to close in requirement of highly maneuverable adversaries. He has gone to the men who have "been there" in his considerable research efforts, and he does a fine job of translating pilot and aeronautical engineering lingo into layman's language.

The F-14, as the first new true fighter type to be introduced into the U.S. inventory in some years, was a long time in coming. This book gives a good background picture of the principal reasons for this modernization delay. I think you will find it a most readable and informative work.

ROBERT B. BALDWIN
Vice Admiral, U.S. Navy

Preface

This book was supposed to be a quaint picture book about the Navy's latest jet fighter. I had little idea of what would unfold as I started my research. It was my honest belief that the project could be done in six months. In fact it took a year and a half. One of the reasons it took this long was the complexity of the aircraft itself.

The amount of time necessary to learn fighter aerodynamics turned out to be much longer than it takes simply to study the forces on a wing that most private pilots learn. Fighter pilots need to know turn rate, turn radius, P_s, instantaneous G and other now familiar terms. I became convinced that there was a need for an explanation of this kind of information in order to fully understand the F-14. There seemed to be no middle ground between the simplified private pilot aerodynamics and that taught to aeronautical engineers. Hopefully there is now.

The small size of this book was a frustration. I would like to have gone into more detail and covered wider areas in the history of the F-14. One friend criticized the book for making the Navy and Grumman look too good. He alluded to contract problems, and the politics that one might imagine goes on with a contract involving large amounts of money. Another friend complained that I didn't have any information on the engine problems. This is a small book. To deprive the reader of all the positive information about the F-14 to put in information that casts a shadow on it will have to be saved for another book. I didn't mean to ignore the problems that the F-14 has had, but when it is compared with previous aircraft during the development stage the F-14 stands way out in front.

The pleasure of doing a book on a contemporary aircraft is the availablility of research data. The frustration is that every week adds new information that can make your book passe unless the information is included. I decided that the former route was for me. I'll leave the history of the F-14 for someone in the future. Hopefully, however, the research I've done while the retrieval was easy will make his or her job easier.

Acknowledgements

When I started this book on the F-14 I needed a lot of help. With the help of these people particularly and other friends I was able to take their knowledge and hopefully condense it in a readable form. My thanks to you all and particularly:

Andy Hubbard for his help in the history and photographs; **Norm Gandia** without whose constant attention, help, correspondence, and gracious accommodation I couldn't have done it; **Ray Wagner** for comments and good advice; **Joe Burke, Bob Smythe, Chuck Sewell & Roger Fergurson** for sitting around the table and giving me the pilot's and NFO's point of view; **Bob Laidlaw** for making me an "instant expert" on aerodynamics and always having time to do it; **CAPT Scotty Lamoreaux USN (ret.)** for opening the door; **RADM Swoose Snead USN** for keeping the door open; **Howard Ruggles** for making me aware of limited real estate and commonality; **Sam Ammons** for hours on the back seat and computers; **LT Jeff Punches USN** for consistently dropping interesting tidbits; **Mike Pelehach** for his time and valuable assistance; **Mike Ciminera** for constant attention, input, help and good conversation; **Dick Milligan** for keeping those slides and prints coming my way; **VADM Robert Baldwin USN** for placing me on the deck of the USS *Enterprise* to see what Naval Aviation is all about: **CDR Jack Ready USN** for making a deeper insight into fighter aviation possible; **Bob Lawson** for photo assistance above and beyond the call of duty; **LCDR Kurt Strauss USN** for giving me use of his skipper, squadron, and especially his time; **CAPT Carroll Smith, Jr. USN** for insights into carrier aviation that could only come from the man in charge; **RADM Obie Oberg USN** a straight shooter and giver of strategic insight; **CAPT Jim Foster USN** who said he only had twenty minutes and gave me four hours; **CDR Sam Leeds USN** for sharing his F-4 concept and the air order of battle; **Arnold Whitaker & Bob Kress** for insights into the world beyond; **Bob Steele** for inputs on computers; **Joe Beattie** for a perfect tour; **Robert Carisle** for photo assistance; **CDR Bill Collins USN** who was always ready to help; **RADM Bill Myers USN** for comments from a blackshoe; **ENS Tim Taylor USN** for help on the USS *Enterprise*; **LT Stoney Lightstone USN** for being so helpful; **Fred Dresch** for lending so much photo assistance; **Dale Osborne** for making important photos available; **LCDR Jim Lang USN & Instructional Systems Development (ISD)** for making pictures available that I would have never been able to produce; **Bill Brinks** for his objectivity, Eagle eyes, and encouragement; **CDR Smoke Wilson USN** for hours of input on aerodynamics and other topics; **CDR Jim Taylor USN** for spending time on the USS *Enterprise*; **Navy Fighter Weapons School Staff** for all their help in making me understand what a fighter is all about; **CDR Don Hubbard USN (ret.)** for showing me how to write; **Col. Edwin F. Carey, USAF (ret.)** who fostered my aviation interest and whose dedication to aviation has been a guiding inspiration; **George Skurla** for turning his boys loose on me; **Mike Harris** for reading the ms and giving me feedback; **Harry Gann** for use of some excellent photos; **ADM Issac Kidd USN** for starting me in the right direction; **LT Ed Allen USN** for giving me an insight I probably would never have seen; **LT Steve Miller USN** for excellent photos; and **LT Randy Cunningham USN** for insights into the F-14 and fighters in general.

The Navy's newest and oldest active duty fighter jets fly formation. The F-8 Crusader *and the F-14* Tomcat *represent over twenty years spread in aerospace technology.*   (Harry Gann Photo)

The Douglas F6D Missileer *was a subsonic airplane designed to carry eight* Eagle *missiles. The* Missileer's *role would have been Fleet Air Defense, but since it could perform no other role, it was never produced.* (McDonnell Douglas Corporation)

The History of Development

The F-14A *Tomcat* represents the culmination of the U.S. Navy's drive for a total air superiority fighter through the use of an advanced airframe with a variable sweep wing and a long range weapon system. In a little less than two years from the signing of the F-14 contract, the F-14 made its first flight. On December 21, 1972, almost a month ahead of schedule, Grumman chief test pilot Bob Smyth rolled down the runway at Grumman's Calverton plant with project test pilot Bill Miller in the back seat. In spite of a setback caused by the crash of *Tomcat* No. 1 on 30 December 1970, VF-124, the fleet readiness training squadron, received its first F-14 in June of 1972. The first two F-14 fleet squadrons, VF-1 and VF-2 were commissioned on October 14, 1972 at NAS Miramar. These two squadrons deployed on the USS Enterprise in September, 1974, and spent eight months deployed in the Western Pacific and Indian Ocean, returning in May, 1975.

The concept began during the 1950s when, studying the Russian threat, the Navy assessed their requirement to be a subsonic aircraft that could deliver multiple shots at multiple long range targets. The answer became an "on

paper" airplane known as the Douglas F6D *Missileer*. The *Missileer* would carry the two-stage *Eagle* missile (XAAM-M-10) with active homing radar guidance, a high power pulse Doppler and a track-while-scan missile control system.[1] This track-while-scan system would give the F6D a multiple shot capability when carrying the *Eagle* missiles. The high straight wing permitted external installation of six *Eagle* missiles; and the basic arrangement of the Douglas Model D-766 permitted installation of two missiles on the forward lower fuselage for a total of eight missiles.[2]

The engines for the Douglas F6D *Missileer* were the newly designed Pratt and Whitney turbofan TF30-P-2.[3] The turbofan, specifically designed for fuel endurance, was a departure from the traditional turbojet. The newly developed airframe by Douglas and the developing fan jet engine by Pratt and Whitney were being developed as a platform for the *Eagle* missile. Bendix was the major *Eagle* contractor, with Grumman in charge of the airframe design and development.

The Tu-28 Fiddler *is one of the many Soviet aircraft capable of launching air-to-air and air-to-surface missiles.   (U.S. Navy)*

The *Eagle-Missileer* program was cancelled in December of 1960 because the Department of Defense believed that the F6D would be able to perform only one mission. Then as now, cost effectiveness of an aircraft was an important hurdle during development.

The Threat

The design of any aircraft and the accompanying systems is a function of the present or projected threat. The threat of World War II was usually another aircraft or anti-aircraft ground fire. Today it has become multi-dimensional with missiles coming from other aircraft, ships, and submarines.

Cruise Missile Threat

The U.S. Navy learned how important control of the air was during World War II. As a result, the Navy has emphasized the development of the aircraft carrier. The Russians, on the other hand, have pressed vigorously with a large family of offensive air-to-surface and surface-to-surface cruise missiles. The Russians developed the cruise missile to act as an equalizer against the American advantage of the aircraft carrier and ship fire power.

Surface-to-surface cruise missiles have some distinct advantages over carriers. They keep low to the curvature of the earth, making it difficult for the ship's defensive radars to pick them up until they are too close. The surface-to-surface cruise missile entered operational service as a relatively simple piece of hardware. However, through it has evolved a more sophisticated guided weapon capable of diverse trajectories. They can be deployed by submarines and any size ship, which gives smaller ships increased fire power and multiplies the threat to the fleet.

Cruise missiles are also carried by airborne Russian bombers. The Russians have developed sophisticated Mach 2 bombers capable of launching cruise air-to-surface missiles with a long range stand-off capability. These missiles have a range from 50 to over 200 miles. In some cases, the ship's radar may not be able to pick up the launching bomber. The defense of this threat falls clearly on the fleet defense role of the aircraft carrier's fighters. However, the ability to counter the bomber threat is not enough. Once the cruise air-to-surface missile has been launched, an effective method of dealing with the anti-ship missiles must exist.

Because of the earth hugging capabilities

A MiG-21D Fishbed *in flight.*   *(U.S. Navy)*

of these two major threats, the air-to-surface and surface-to-surface missiles, the airplane becomes the logical extension of the ship's radar and weapons. With the extended range of the airplane's radar at altitude, the airplane's weapons have the potential to counter the cruise missile further out. The cruise missile is more easily seen by airborne Doppler radar, and with the proper missile, can defeat it. It was with this Doppler radar look-down capability and the *Eagle* missile that the F6D *Missileer* would have countered the then cruise missile threat.

The Aircraft Threat

The obvious threat in a tactical situation is the enemy's fighter. Control of the air as a dominant factor in successful warfare is no longer questioned. The Russians have learned this historical lesson and have been pursuing the development of first class fighters.

For a long time, the Russian philosophy was to build a short legged, highly maneuverable aircraft. The aircraft could be short legged because its only mission was the defense of its homeland. There was not the need for penetrating long distances and threading through hostile territory: the ground control intercept controllers (GCI) could lead the planes right to the targets. Since this has been historically the case, the airplanes that the U.S. has encountered in Korea (the MiG-15) and in Vietnam (MiGs 17, 19, and 21) have been this classic short-legged, highly agile clear air mass fighters. These fighters didn't have the long range fuel requirements, could be built

smaller, and were therefore difficult to see. They follow all the rules of what an ideal day fighter aircraft should be: small, agile and carry a gun.[4]

The Russian design philosophy for building fighter aircraft is changing. Just as the political-military shift changed the naval fleet from home defense to offensive warships for projection of power so has the design of fighter aircraft changed.[5] Most of the new fighters are all-weather aircraft, with increased fuel for deep penetration. The less sophisticated MiG-17, MiG-19, and MiG-21 will continue to be a threat because they can be deployed in such great numbers and are exported to client nations. Communist countries have built thousands of MiG-17s. A relatively fewer number of MiG-19s were built, but thousands of MiG-21s have also lifted off the runway. Even the United States Marines couldn't ignore the bow and arrow if they were outnumbered 100 to 1. Admiral Thomas Moorer, former Chairman of the Joint Chiefs of Staff, in a mid-1973 speech, stated that these aircraft, MiGs 17 through 21, will make up only 35 per cent of the home defense aircraft.

The Russians have been making strides toward becoming first in air superiority. At the Domodedovo Air Show outside Moscow in 1967, the Russians displayed 12 new aircraft designs.[6] In the period from the mid-fifties to the early seventies, the Russians have introduced over twenty fighters. Eight are operational.[7] During that same time period the U.S. has introduced the F-4 *Phantom*, back in the mid-fifties, the F-111 and F-5 *Freedom Fighter* in the mid-sixties.

11

THE TFX

The F-111 (TFX), born out of disagreement, developed into a political battle that still echoes within the Military-Industrial Complex. A version of the TFX, the F-111B, was supposed to be the Navy's solution to Fleet Air Defense. In fact, the F-111B just postponed the solution.

In 1959, General F. F. Everest, the new commander of the USAF's Tactical Air Command (TAC), wanted a new fighter-bomber that could perform the role of the F-105. The F-105 could only operate out of a limited number of foreign airfields. TAC wanted this limitation solved. As a result, TAC was specific about wanting the new plane to land in half the distance of the F-105. The new fighter-bomber would also have to fly non-stop un-refueled to Europe and to Southeast Asia with only one refueling. General Everest also wanted a treetop 1000 mph dash for 400 miles and a high altitude dash speed of 1700 mph.[8] These requirements were modified the following spring in the form of Specific Operational Requirement 183 (SOR).[9]

During this same time, the Navy was working on its requirement for Fleet Air Defense (FAD). The F6D *Missileer/Eagle* was proceeding when Secretary of Defense, Thomas Gates, cancelled the project in December, 1960. The *Eagle* missile continued for a short time after that.

When Robert Strange McNamara took office in January of 1961, he wasted little time unleashing his famous "Whiz kids," which one Air Force Colonel called "Bow Tie Bastards." One of the overriding concepts that McNamara pushed was commonality. He felt that by applying this approach, he could save the country and services millions of dollars, and still give them what they needed.

Through the office of the Director of Defense Research and Engineering (DDR&E), McNamara recommended that the Air Force and the Navy seriously consider combining their two missions — Fleet Air Defense for the Navy, and high Mach, low level interdiction for the Air Force — into one airplane. However, the mission descriptions alone called for two different airplanes. The Navy's requirement called for a plane that could physically fit on a carrier and be light enough to take off and land there too. From the beginning the Navy maintained that their Fleet Air Defense requirements were not compatible with the aircraft that the Air Force said it needed. McNamara didn't budge. He insisted that the two services *would* combine their requirements into one plane. Commonality was the buzz word. The Air Force held fast to their requirement for a 1.2 Mach tree-top dash speed. The Navy was unbudging in its requirement for the *Eagle* missile and the defensive stand-off capability that the F6D/*Eagle* had represented.

The F-111B rolls out for its first public appearance. It first flew on May 18, 1965.   *(Grumman)*

The swing wing of the F-111B was basically a take-off and landing, or cruise device. They could be set in various sweep angles for different missions. The wing was operated manually, and was not designed to be operated under heavy G loads. In this photo, notice the leading edge slats and trailing edge flaps. F-111B shows its variable sweep wings. (Grumman)

The *Eagle* missile was cancelled due to political factors during the beginning discussions of the joint service use of the F-111. The need for the long range *Eagle* missile was so important to the Navy that it reappeared, rising out of the ashes of the *Eagle* program as the *Phoenix* missile.[10] The weapon system conceived for the *Missileer* now had a name — AWG-9. The AWG-9, like the *Phoenix*, would be developed by Hughes. To study the specific Navy requirements for the TFX and to re-examine the case for the F-111B, the Navy formed Navy Fighter Study I. The results of the Fighter Study showed that the case for the F-111B to carry the *Phoenix* was indisputable.[11]

The F-111B began flying May 18, 1965 and immediately started having problems. The engine inlets caused compressor stalls in certain parts of the performance envelope. Next the F-111B started having weight problems. The Navy became upset. It had always

had a good working relationship with Grumman, in fact, when Grumman was announced November 26th, 1962 as the contract winner along with General Dynamics (who would build the Air Force version) the Navy felt some sense of relief. Nevertheless, the F-111 program continued to be an Air Force run program, and the Air Force did not have the weight restriction the Navy did.

The F-111B became a political thorn in McNamara's side. During the summer of 1966 McNamara started calling Saturday morning meetings every two weeks to seek a solution to these legitimate but embarrassing problems.[12] All the heavyweights were there, including the chairmen of the boards of the respective contractors, the secretaries of the Navy and Air Force as well as the Deputy Secretary of Defense. Nevertheless the reports kept flowing back to Washington: the F-111B is unsatisfactory. The test pilots complained they couldn't see the carrier on approach due to the angle of attack and the angle of the windshield which caused a serious reflection problem. The weight was excessive which created another problem since the arresting gear on the carrier wasn't stressed for a plane of F-111B's size. The wind that the carrier could put over the deck under certain conditions wasn't enough for a safe catapult shot. The complaints kept coming. All this from a new swing wing aircraft with a new turbofan engine and weapons system that was supposed to be everybody's answer.

The Colossal Weight Improvement Program (CWIP) was an attempt to strip the F-111B of as much weight as possible. While the Super Weight Improvement Program was internal changes only, the CWIP involved major structural revisions. This F-111B model appears foreshortened, but it isn't – it's appearance is a result of these major changes. Notice also the engine mounted pylon for the Phoenix. *(Grumman)*

A program was instituted to correct these and other deficiencies. The improved bird was called the Navy II F-111B. It moved the landing gear aft, put on a new nose and put in a P-5 engine.[13] The Navy's original requirement was for a 50,000 pound airplane, but the final General Dynamics proposal called for a plane of 63,500 pounds. The first plane produced by Grumman was over 70,000 pounds as a result of trying to make commonality work.[14] A weight improvement program was started called SWIP for Super Weight Improvement Program. It managed to remove about three thousand pounds with internal changes. The SWIP F-111B looked the same externally. After the SWIP attempt, Grumman initiated another weight reduction program. This was called CWIP for Colossal Weight Improvement Program. The CWIP program was an attempt to do radical surgery externally and internally. At the same time,

Close-up look at the Phoenix *missile's movable pylon on the F-111B. The Grumman designed F-14 avoided the movable pylon problem by mounting the* Phoenix *missiles under the belly and on the stationary glove area.   (U.S. Navy)*

Grumman was working on a Navy funded Anti-Air Warfare Study. This study was to determine what could be done to get the F-111B back to where it would accomplish the Navy's mission. The projected 16,000 pounds of internal fuel needed to do the mission had jumped to 26,000 pounds to carry the overweight F-111B for its originally designed mission.

The problem was getting beyond anyone's control; the Navy was not being quiet about their feelings. While all the commotion about the F-111B was going on, the Navy funded some money for advanced fighter studies to Grumman.

The F-111B with a Phoenix *missile under its left wing. The mechanism that kept the* Phoenix *missile parallel to the free airstream was complicated, heavy, and didn't always work. (Navy)*

In October of 1967 Grumman went to the Navy with a proposal. The proposal recommended a way to wrap a new airframe around the existing F-111B avionic and engines. The new airframe would lighten the load and fulfill the other fighter role, that of air superiority. The weight would be reduced by the increased use of titanium and the efficient use of engineering design concepts. The Grumman recommendation became known as the VFX. There were two proposals, the VFX-1 and VFX-2. The VFX-2 would use an Advanced Technology Engine (ATE) that was under development as a joint Navy and Air Force project.

The Navy reacted to Grumman's VFX proposal with another study group, Navy Fighter Study II. Between February and May 1968, the Navy compared the proposed VFX with the F-111B. They studied the two missions, Fleet Air Defense and the Other Fighter Role.[15] The Study showed that the VFX was vastly superior in many areas. The VFX-1 (Grumman design 303-60) had 10 times the rate of climb at 40,000 feet. The F-111B's time to accelerate at altitude from .8 to 1.8 Mach was over 6 minutes. By comparison, the F-4 *Phantom II* had a 50 percent greater acceleration than the F-111B. The VFX-1 with the same engines as the F-111B could accelerate over 60 percent faster than the F-4 from .8 to 1.8 Mach. At 35,000 feet the VFX-1 could accelerate from .8 to 1.8 Mach in around 2 minutes. The soon to be born F-14 would turn in 50 percent less time than the F-111B. The Navy Fighter Study II group was overwhelmed by the superior performance of the VFX-1 in the Other Fighter Role, that of air superiority, and it was this better performance that broke the F-111B's back.[16] In May of 1968, Congress wrote the swan song to the F-111B: They cancelled the funds.

In July 1968, a Request for Proposals (RFP) went out to the aerospace industry for the VFX. These were the basic requirements:

1. Two-man crew, tandem seating. A fighter mission is characterized by a series of tasks ranging from navigation to kill assessment. The crew members must carry out these tasks against an enemy who is equipped with sophisticated ECM, surface-to-air missiles, and fighters. While the VFX carries various sensors to maximize crew awareness, monitoring these sensors requires head-down attention. The two-man crew divides these tasks between them, so that one pair of eyes is always at head-up.

2. Two engines. Operating safety, efficiency, weapon mounting, duct

simplicity, engine accessibility, and growth potential were key factors in selecting a 2-engine design. Pratt & Whitney TF30-P-412 engines were to be utilized.

3. Advanced weapon control system. Navy analyses concluded that in the fleet air defense mission at least 75% more fighters with single-shot systems are required to match the capabilities of fighters with the AWG-9 track-while-scan/multi-shot Phoenix system. It was also concluded that against air- or surface-launched antiship missiles, a high-powered track-while-scan radar with long-range, multishot missiles was necessary for adequate defense.

4. Armament. Phoenix missiles (6); Sparrow 7F (6) or 7E missiles; Sidewinder missiles (4) plus one internal M-61A gun.

5. Design flight conditions. High fighter limit load factors exceeding those of the F4J Phantom with Sparrow and Phoenix missiles.

6. Carrier suitability. Landing strength for six Phoenix missiles and 4000 lb. of fuel. Landing speeds and weights of VFX are suitable for operation from the Hancock class CVAs.[17]

North American Rockwell, LTV, Grumman, McDonnell Douglas, and General Dynamics responded. Grumman and McDonnell Douglas were announced as the finalists in December of 1968. The Defense Department awarded Grumman the F-14A contract in January of 1969. The Contract was signed February 3, 1969.

The F-14 is Born

Grumman had been out of the fighter business since their F-11F *Tiger*. The *Tiger* first flew in 1954 and final production stopped in 1958. However, Grumman probably had more experience than any other aerospace company with swing wing technology. On May 19th, 1952, the variable geometry XF-10F *Jaguar* made its first flight. It was this technology plus Grumman's historical relationship with the Navy that made Grumman the major sub-contractor to General Dynamics, and primary builder of the F-111B.

The XF10F-1 Jaguar was Grumman's first attempt at swing wing technology. The knowledge gained with the Jaguar was partly responsible for Grumman's getting the F-111B contract, (also a swing wing aircraft), and the contract for the F-14. The Bell X-5 was the first airplane to fly with a variable sweep wing.   (Grumman) (Bell Aerospace Company, a Division of Textron)

Swing wing technology started with the German P1101. The P1101 was a swing wing prototype, whose wing could only be moved on the ground. World War II ended before the P1101 could fly. In 1952, the Bell X-5 was the first swing wing airplane to fly. Shortly after the X-5, Grumman launched the XF-10F. There were many problems associated with swing wings that were to be ironed out in the F-111B and optimized in the F-14.

The F-14 as we know it today is the result of refinement that spanned a time period from before the Request for Proposal in June of 1968 to the Design Configuration Freeze in March of 1969. The history of the evolution is an interesting story. It is probably best told by the men that directed its progress.

Actually, our studies of over 6,000 configurations boiled down to eight specific design numbers: 303-60, 303A, 303B, 303C, 303D, 303E, 303F and 303G.

Design 303-60, of January, 1968, had podded engines and a high variable-sweep wing like our winning 303E (F-14) design. But it was more an assemblage of reasonable goals than a mature blend of aerodynamics, structures, electronics, and airframe subsystems.

During the five months after we presented 303-60 to the Navy, extensive design, wind tunnel test, and analytical studies proceeded in parallel examinations of alternate configurations. Design 303A, a minor nacelle modification of the original 303-60, was updated to become 303B. This was an intermediate development of the podded configuration, lying between 303-60 and the winning 303E design. Design 303C also had a high variable-sweep wing, but submerged, rather than podded, engines. Design 303D had submerged engines but a low variable-sweep wing, and 303F had a fixed wing.

The Grumman proposed VFX model 303-60 which was to replace the F-111B. A minor nacelle modification made it the 303A. Additional modifications made it evolve into the 303B. (Grumman)

Design 303 G had podded engines, and a high variable-sweep wing. But it was a "fighter only" version with AWG-10 fire control system and four Sparrows. Without Phoenix capability, it was discarded.

The 303D design was dropped for several reasons, but ". . . poor subsonic longitudinal stability, poor subsonic drag due to lift, excessive cruise fuel flow, and reduced maximum afterburner supersonic thrust," were the major ones.

Next we compared the submerged-engine 303C design to the podded 303B. Both had a high variable-sweep wing and were about equal in weight and carrier suitability. But we discarded the C because the B proved superior in:

Grumman VFX design 303C.　　(Grumman)

- installed fuel flow and maximum afterburner thrust;
- supersonic combat ceiling performance;
- isolated inlets and nozzles, precluding F-111B maximum-performance engine troubles;
- large spacing between inlet and fuselage, requiring no boundary layer diverter system;
- growth potential for installation of "advanced technology" engines.

The B was modified . . . to become the contract-award-winning E, which we then ran off against the fixed-wing 303F. The F lost for two major reasons:

- Its takeoff gross weight would have been 4,920 pounds heavier for the Sparrow fighter mission than the E, primarily because of the larger (745 square feet) wing area provided for

Grumman VFX design 303D.　　(Grumman)

carrier suitability. The fixed-wing still did not meet carrier suitability requirements for the 6-Phoenix Combat Air Patrol mission with the double-slotted-flap high-lift system assumed. Boundary layer control also would have been required, further increasing its weight. Wave-off single-engine rate of climb was also unacceptable, due to the low wing-span.
- The large wing area and high-lift system degraded low-altitude performance.[18]

The initial design 303-60 evolved into the award winning 303E.

Grumman VFX design 303F with the fixed wing. *(Grumman)*

One of the reasons for the Grumman success in using the swing wing is the high percentage of titanium, approximately 25 per cent in the airplane, but specifically, the all titanium wing box that the wings attach to.

Many aeronautical engineers are skeptical of welding as a legitimate aerospace technique. They feel that bolted-up structures are a more conservative approach and hence, safer. The wing box in the F-111B was made of steel in the bolted-up fashion. As an alternative to the bolted up method, Grumman investigated a welding process called electron-beam welding. This process fuses two pieces of titanium into their

The all-titanium box beam absorbs the transmitted wing loads. The box beam also acts as a fuel tank. In the background is one of the vacuum chambers in which the electron beam welding takes place. *(Grumman)*

18

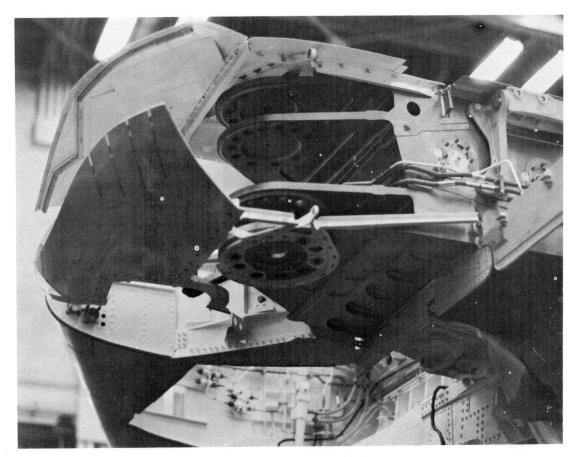

The two pair of wing hinges extend from the all-titanium box beam. Either pair can have one hinge fail with no failure to the integrity of the wing.   *(Flight International)*

molecular components with a strength loss of only 3 per cent, a loss factor very acceptable to the conservative Grumman engineers. The F-14A has saved 900 pounds on the box beam with the Grumman pioneered electron-beam welding process of titanium. Titanium has a higher strength to weight ratio than steel. It was steel that was used in the F-111B wing box. The F-111B wing box had a history of problems, so Grumman was putting the reputation of its infamous Iron Works on the line when they advocated this radical departure from bolted-up procedures. The move to the electron beam process proved to be a great success. In fact, the wing box from the first pre-production aircraft that crashed on December 30, 1970 was found six feet underground virtually undamaged.

The F-4 used approximately 9 per cent titanium, compared to the 24.4 per cent used by the F-14. Titanium is a difficult metal to work with, and for that reason has been used only to a limited degree in the past. It is very hard, in fact much harder than steel. Yet,

titanium is lighter than steel. The strength to weight of titanium is so much greater than steel, Grumman uses titanium to carry the loads in the upper and lower wing panels. Titanium is so different to work with than steel, that it requires a different angle drillbit. The drill must be stabilized by a machine, for if a man tried to drill a hole by hand into titanium, the drill would dance around on top of the metal. The area where the hole will be drilled must be flooded with freon gas to chill it, otherwise the titanium heats up to the brittle point and loses all its strength.

The wing is completely wet. When the computerized holes are drilled, and the rivets placed into the upper and lower wing panels, they are water, or in this case kerosene tight. There is no sealer. The rivets are slightly larger than the hole. The rivets are slammed into the holes with such force and accuracy, they fuse into the metal. The rest of the F-14 is made up of approximately 40 per cent *aluminum alloy*, less than 1 per cent *boron*, and about 18 per cent *steel*.

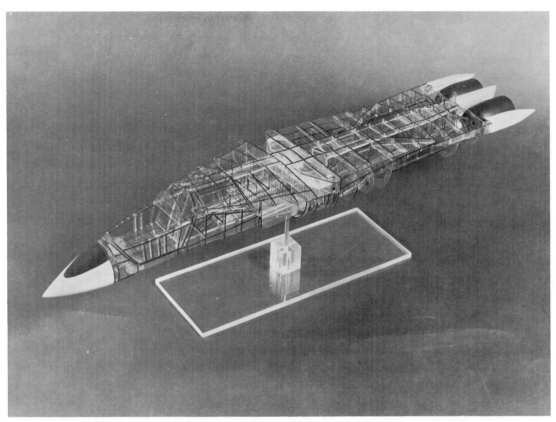

Comparing the structures of the F-111B and the F-14, the most obvious difference is in the F-14's carrying the gear within the fuselage structure. This, plus the tandem seating, allows for fuselage-length longerons for strength, and avoids the large added weight of beefed-up structures needed on the F-111B.   (Grumman)

The days of the simple F 6F are over. The Grumman *Hellcat* was a threatening airplane in its day. Its 50 calibre machine guns were enough to handle the threat. Its gross weight was 15,413 pounds, or about 600 pounds less than the weight of the F-14's internal fuel. The F-14's gross weight is about that of a World War II B-24 bomber.

Mass alone is not the major contrasting feature between the World War II F-6F and the F-14. The *Tomcat* has four unique features: the swing wing, the integrated AWG-9 Weapons System, the *Phoenix* missile, and the integrated computer system. One additional feature distinguishes the F-6F *Hellcat* of World War II and today's F-14. This feature talks, turns his head to check the rear, relieves the pilot of some workload and is called a Naval Flight Officer.* The NFO has been around for some time, and the Navy is sold on his value as a result of F-4 *Phantom* experience in Vietnam.

The F-4 *Phantom* was the first Navy fighter to use the NFO concept. The F-4 developed out of the philosophy that dogfights were a thing of the past. The F-4 would eliminate the dogfight by sending out a missile in its place and the pilot wouldn't have to visually see his target. This great leap forward was premature in its attempt to use radar as a set of eyes. It was premature due to the state of the art, the arena of battle, and because the politicians didn't leave the war to the military. They required our pilots during the Vietnam war to visually identify almost every target. These rules of engagement caused the *Phantom* to end up in dogfights, the very scenario that it was designed to overcome. The Navy learned quickly that it was a mistake to buy or design an airplane that was not capable of air combat maneuvering (ACM).

*The term NFO (Naval Flight Officer) refers to all non-pilot officers on flight status (Medical Corps excepted). An NFO can be riding in the tail-end of an EC-121 or other fixed wing and helicopter aircraft, the back seat of an EA-6B or behind an F-14 pilot. Testimony to the NFO's status in the Navy lies in the fact that CDR Denny Strole, USN, the Third Commanding Officer of VF-1 (and during the F-14's first deployment) is an NFO. NFO's in F-4 *Phantoms* have been called RIOs for Radar Intercept Officers. Hughes Aircraft Co., not to be outdone, dubbed the backseater the NCO or Missile Control Officer. After seeing NCO in the company-produced literature, and in the aircraft, RADM Snead, F-14 Program Manager said, "What's with this MCO? The guy in back is not an MCO or an RIO — he's an NFO!" Nevertheless there are still NFO's who want to be singled out as *Phantom* NFO's and object to being called anything but an RIO.

An F-14 from VF-1 is hoisted aboard the USS Enterprise *at NAS Alameda for Fleet Deployment, September 1974.*

As a result, the F-14 took the premature F-4 idea and matured it. The F-14 was designed as an air Superiority aircraft, without compromising its other missions. The F-4 carried two types of missiles — the heat seeking *Sidewinder* for short range targets (a thousand feet to a couple of miles) and the radar-oriented *Sparrow* medium range missile. In simplistic terms, the F-14 expanded the F-4's capabilities in two directions. Outwardly, it added the long range *Phoenix* missile. For close in work, the Tomcat has a gun, the M61 20 mm cannon. The Navy's F-4s never had a gun. The F-14, then, becomes a flexible flying weapons platform, capable of fighting like its greatgrandfather, the *Hellcat* or performing the mission of a stand-off fleet defense interceptor.

One of the major reasons for the F-14's ability in all missions is the AWG-9 multiple target tracking system built by Hughes Aircraft Co. This system allows the NFO to track, with the aid of a computer, up to 24 targets. He can select six targets to fire at under simultaneous attack with the Phoenix missile. The selection can be made by the NFO or the computer in the AWG-9 can select the firing priorities. Another alternative is Data Link. Data Link is a no-voice, and in the case of the F-14A, two-way communication device that will let the Air Warfare commander on the ship dictate which targets are the priorities. The ship, through Data Link, can also display an additional 8 targets on the NFO's Tactical Information Display (TID). This coordination with the complement of ships, and their powerful computers, allows the Combat Information Center (CIC) of the surface fleet to work with an overall picture that they never have had in the past. The range and power of the AWG-9 radar gives the surface fleet a significantly bigger picture than the F-4 did and therefore more time to respond.

The F-14 also has an AWG-9 radar mode designed for the visual attack. This mode allows the pilot to fire his short range, heat-seeking *Sidewinder* missile or *Sparrow* missile in the ACM mode, before he has finished the turn in a dogfight. In the past, the F-4 had to almost point its nose on the target to get a valid shot. With the F-14 this is no longer necessary. However, the F-14 has the ability to follow any threat aircraft, without using this radar mode, by relying on its inherent aerodynamic capabilities.

Development of major weapon systems in the post Korean War era that tried to integrate new airframes, new engines, and new avionics usually ran into problems. The

Navy and Grumman engineers decided to take the conservative approach in building the F-14. The Navy and Grumman took a proven engine in the TF 30, a known AWG-9 weapons system from the F-111B and wrapped a new airframe around these two proven commodities. The second generation F-14B would keep the same airframe, the same avionics, but was to use the Advanced Technology Engine, the Pratt & Whitney F401. The F-14C is designed to be the same as the F-14B but with new, state of the art, avionics.

In a little less than two years from the signing of the F-14 contract, the F-14 made its first flight. On December 21, 1972, almost a month ahead of schedule, Grumman chief test pilot Bob Smyth rolled down the runway at Grumman's Calverton plant with project test pilot Bill Miller in the back seat. In spite of a setback caused by the crash of *Tomcat* No. 1 on 30 December 1970, VF-124, the fleet readiness training squadron, received its first F-14 in June of 1972. The first two F-14 fleet squadrons, VF-1 and VF-2 were commissioned on October 14, 1972 at NAS Miramar. These two squadrons deployed on the *USS Enterprise* in September, 1974.

The first F-14 Tomcat lands on USS Enterprise *during operations off the California coast March 18, 1974.*   *(U.S. Navy)*

F-14 Physical and Aerodynamic Characteristics

External View of the F-14

When looking at the F-14, several features stand out. The twin vertical tails are probably the first feature. This design has several advantages over the single tail. Two shorter tails, as opposed to a single taller tail is an advantage on an aircraft carrier where there is a height limit on the carrier hangar deck. Two tails have an advantage if one gets shot off during battle. The separate tails give good single engine stability; they create part of the package that makes the F-14 spin resistant.

A VF-2 Tomcat cruises with wings aft above the clouds west of San Diego over the Pacific Ocean.
(Robert L. Lawson)

Three F-14s come into the break at NAS Miramar. The wings would ordinarily be further forward if the automatic wing schedule were on. The pilots traditionally put the wing sweep into the manual mode, sweep the wings full aft, bank, and then pop back into the automatic schedule. (Robert L. Lawson) Three F-14A pre-production aircraft fly in formation with their wings in various sweep configurations. Aircraft number 2 is full forward at 20° – the takeoff and landing configuration – number 4 is a 45°, and number 1 is a full aft 68° sweep . In the manual mode the pilot cannot select a sweep angle that will overstress the structural limit for a given airspeed. (Grumman)

Another feature that distinguishes the F-14 is visible in flight. It's dramatic to watch the F-14 break over an airfield and see the wings sweep forward as the airspeed bleeds off. The wings sweep from 20° full forward to 68° back in flight. On the flightdeck the wings will oversweep to 75° to reduce the amount of space the F-14 takes up. This variable-sweep wing lets the F-14 dash at Mach 2.5 or land at 115 knots. One Navy official claimed that the F-14 could land at 60 knots except that high angle of attack would cause the tail pipes to drag the ground.[19]

The rectangular inlets are usually the next noticed shape. They are offset from the fuselage to avoid any turbulence usually generated by the junction of the body to engine inlet. The two-dimensional horizontal shape was the easiest shape for designing a scheduling ramp. The ramp travels up and down depending on the Mach number of the aircraft. So far, the aerospace industry has not designed an engine that can accept supersonic air. The scheduling ramp moves up and down so that the air always enters at medium subsonic speeds. The ramp is controlled by a computer called the Air Inlet Control System (AICS). This computer is isolated and independent from the rest of the aircraft's computers. The ramp goes up and down as a function of Mach number. As the speed of the F-14 increases, the ramp starts down. This action takes advantage of Bernoulli's principle which describes the action of a fluid (in this case air), i.e., that it slows down as it expands into an area of greater volume.

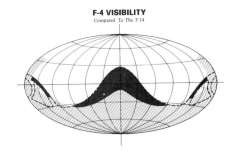

F-4 VISIBILITY
Compared To The F-14

The F-4A pictured directly above was designed as a pure interceptor. Notice the flush canopy. The F-4B and follow-on design modifications bumped up the canopy as shown in the insert above right. Above left the insert shows the relative visibility of the F-14 compared with the F-4.

(Robert L. Lawson photo/McDonnell Douglas & U.S. Navy)

The visibility out of the F-4 *Phantom* isn't what a fighter pilot would design. But, then, the F-4 was not designed for high visibility. Originally, the F-4's canopy was flush with the top of the fuselage because of the Mach 2 + interceptor requirement. Good rearward visibility wasn't necessary, so the thinking went, since speed and radar would take care of the problem threats. Vietnam shattered that illusion.

The F-14 has visibility not experienced in a fighter since the F-86. The entire cockpit is placed on the highest part of the airplane. This gives 360° visibility, and some downward visibility as well. If you compare the F-14 visibility to the Russian threat aircraft, or to most pre-Vietnam airplane designs, the difference is obvious. Pilots have just accepted the rearward blind spots and maneuvered to compensate for them.

The reason, of course, for the faired canopies was to reduce drag and thereby to increase speed. Visibility rearward wouldn't be needed because dogfights were a thing of the past. It's interesting to see how history repeats itself. The early versions of the famous P-51 Mustang had a faired canopy. However, the versions responsible for making its reputation, had a full canopy which gave the pilots a tactical advantage — the ability to see.

The landing gear on the F-14 is the

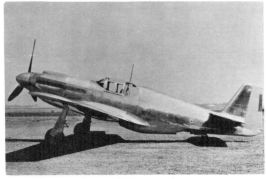

The original P-51 had a canopy flush with the spine of the airplane. However, the versions responsible for the successful kill ratios had the bubble canopy pictured above.

(Robert L. Lawson collection)

25

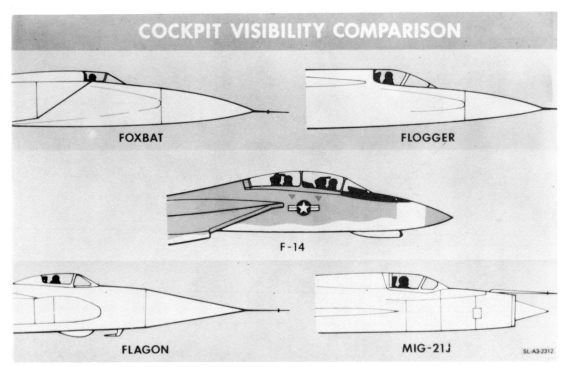

COCKPIT VISIBILITY COMPARISON

FOXBAT

FLOGGER

F-14

FLAGON

MIG-21J

SL-A3-2312

The tactical disadvantages of bad visibility inspired the 360° visibility in the F-14. Contrasted with this advantage is the limited visibility of the threat aircraft. (U.S. Navy/ISD)

beefed-up type that carrier aircraft have to have for the high sink rates. The Naval Aviator does not land an aircraft in the normal airline flared approach. It's more like a controlled crash. At touchdown, the nosewheel is slammed into the deck, while the pilot adds full power. Full power is applied in case the pilot misses the wire.

The landing gear can take a sink rate of 26 feet per second (1560 feet per minute) at a weight of 52,000 pounds. The F-14's sink rate is less than the F-4J's in normal landings. The gear retracts forward. This allows it to fall into the airstream and be blown down into position, should an airborne failure occur.

The main landing gear is part of the glove structure, and not part of nor built into the wing structure as it was in the F-111B. (Flight International)

Flight Controls and Lift/Drag Devices

The F-14 picked up a nickname "The Turkey" during the first fleet squadron carrier qualifications. LCDR Grover (Skip) Giles,* the pilot and his NFO, LCDR Roger McFillen, both from VF-1, were the first flight crew to qualify for daytime carrier operations in March 1974. During their trials aboard the *USS Enterprise*, the F-14 had an unusual appearance on final approach. The stabilators (horizontal stabilizer and elevator combined into one — sometimes called a flying tail) were moving in different directions. The stabilators were moving differentially, and therefore acting as both ailerons and elevators. This tail flapping approach combined with the landing gear sticking out like birds' legs looked like a barnyard turkey to the carrier's crewmen.[20] There are no ailerons in the wing of the F-14. Ailerons would be useless once the variable swept wings were in the swept position. The shift in the aerodynamic center of pressure as a result of wing sweep is another reason for the differential tail. There is some coordination between the differential tail and the spoilers, when the wing sweep position is less than 57 degrees. The spoilers are locked down when the wing position is greater than 57°. Lateral or roll control is then provided only by differential stabilators.[21]

A close-up of the over-wing blending between the box beam and the wing. The segmented spoilers are also visible on the wing.
(Flight International)

The lift/drag devices are mostly on the wing. The two exceptions are the glove vanes, in the glove area, and the speed brakes, above and below the boatail area

*Skip Giles has the dubious distinction of being the first active duty Naval aviator to eject from an F-14. During normal operations his F-14 caught fire and both he and Roger McFillen, his NFO, were forced to eject over the South China Sea on January 2, 1975. Both crewmen were recovered safely.

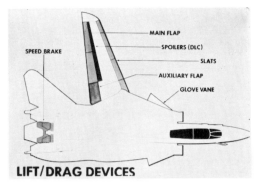

LIFT/DRAG DEVICES

between the tail pipes. The wing has the main flaps, auxiliary flaps, spoilers, and slats. The main flaps and slats are not only used for takeoff and landing but also for air combat maneuvering. The flaps, slats and the glove vanes form the high lift system for takeoff/landing and in-flight maneuvering. The auxiliary or inboard flap is used only during takeoff or landing.

The glove vanes are fully retracted here. They are capable of 15° extension during supersonic flight or can be manually extended subsonically for maneuvering. *(Flight International)*

The glove vanes, like the maneuvering flaps and slats, are extended manually by the Direct Lift Control (DLC)/maneuver flap thumbwheel on the control stick, during subsonic flight. In supersonic flight these functions are automatically done by the Central Air Data Computer (CADC), as a function of altitude and Mach number. The extension of the glove vanes, for example, starts above Mach 1.0 and is deflected to a full 15° at 1.5 Mach. The glove vanes create a lift force forward of the center-of-gravity which compensates for the shift in the wing.

The speed brake is in two parts and three pieces. The upper surface is one piece, and works together with the two separate lower pieces. Extension on both upper and lower speed brakes is to a maximum of 60°. Operating time for extension is 2 seconds.[22]

The nose-gear catapult system differs from the F-4 system. The F-14 has a built-in-holdback fitting that allows a reusable holdback bar. The F-4 uses the classic cable/break-away expendable dumbbell. The F-4 is held in tension with the cable looped around the break-away bar which fits into the fuselage of the F-4. When the catapult reaches the proper tension, the bar breaks, leaving half in the plane, the other on the flight deck. The F-14 is held back by a holdback bar that can be reused 7,500 times.

The F-14 tailhook doesn't have the massive appearance of the F-4's because of the difference in approach speeds. The F-4 slides down the approach path between 140 and 150 knots. The F-14 with the wings swept full forward to 20° comes in around 117 to 120 knots, depending on its weight.

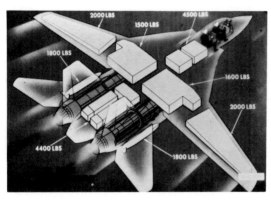

Internal Aircraft Orientation

The F-14 can hold 16,200 pounds of fuel internally. This in conjunction with the low specific fuel consumption of the TF30-P-412A engine allows it to act as its own tanker. It can carry an additional 3,600 pounds externally, for a total of 19,800 pounds. With internal fuel only, the mission profile of the F-14 calls for takeoff, climb to cruise altitude, fly 500 miles, descend to 10,000 feet, fight in maximum afterburner (zone 5) for 2 minutes, climb back to cruise altitude, return to the carrier, loiter overhead for 20 minutes, and land with 5 per cent fuel reserves.[23] This is a significantly greater range than any other fighter today.

Computer Systems

When talking about computers in aircraft, some people think that the computer eliminates the pilot's job — or at least lessens the total work load. Just the opposite is true. The pilot and the NFO are required to do more work in the F-14 than in the F-4. It's true that the computer may lessen the work load for specific jobs in the F-14, but that just lets the Navy add more capabilities and thus more responsibilities.

The original computers in the F-4B *Phantoms* were of the analog type. The inputs and outputs were continuous and were a function of a voltage level. There are still some functions that are done with analog computers, but this is due to the state of the art in those areas.

The most important point to remember when looking at the computers in the F-14 is that they are *integrated.* Integration sounds like a buzz word but it is an important concept. Integration means just what it says — all the different systems can share information with each other. In the F-4 not all the systems could talk to each other. The F-14 has a Computer Signal Data Converter (CSDC) that acts as a central information storage point and disseminator. It sits in the F-14 collecting information waiting for some other instrument, system, or computer to ask for information. Some of the computers can talk directly with each other without going through the CSDC. But for the most part, the CSDC is the hub if you consider the rest of the systems or computers as the end of the spokes. The illustration shows the relationship clearly. The CSDC is not the biggest computer, simple the interface between them all.

Individual Computer Functions

The F-14 has three analog computers. The Automatic Flight Control System (AFCS) is integrated into the primary flight control system. It provides automatic commands for attitude, altitude, heading, and approach modes. The AFCS also provides augmentation for the natural damping characteristics. It is divided into two parts: the Stability Augmentation System (SAS) and the autopilot. The SAS provides augmentation to all three axes. The Fuel Quantity Management System (FQMS) is also a small analog computer.

Another impressive analog computer is the Aileron Rudder Interconnect (ARI). This feature provides spin resistance to the F-14.

To date, there have been only two spins with the F-14, and both have been from the inverted position and pilot induced. At high angles of attack, beyond 24 units,* the rudder interconnects with the AFCS as part of the ARI program to give rudder control only.

The rest of the computers are digital. They work on the binary principle as opposed to the analog (continuous) principle. Probably the most impressive computer is the Hughes Airborne Weapons Group Nine (AWG-9). Its primary function is to identify targets, establish priorities, and monitor approximately 30 black boxes. The AWG-9 processes data to perform intercepts, fire control solutions, initiate weapons, and define launch envelopes. It ends up doing more than just these functions because of extra storage capacity. For example, the AWG-9 performs some navigation solutions.

The Computer Signal Data Converter (CSDC) is one fifth as powerful as the AWG-9. It serves six basic functions. It takes the AWG-9 data and formats it for the rest of the airplane. The CSDC, for example, takes AWG-9 data into the Vertical Display Indicator (VDI) and the Head-Up Display (HUD). Conversely, the CSDC takes the status of systems other than the AWG-9 and presents their data to the AWG-9 for display. The CSDC interfaces the Inertial Navigation System (INS), which is self-contained within the CSDC. All the exchanging of data between the pilot and NFO is done by the CSDC. It performs highly accurate conversions for the AWG-9; and controls the data link to and from the aircraft. It then presents the data to the proper display subsystems.

The computer whose function is most visible, is the one that controls the wing sweep. The Central Air Data Computer (CADC) is designed to make optimum use of all the control surfaces, as well as sweep the wings. It takes inputs from pitot pressure, static pressure, total temperature, and angle of attack data. Most of the other systems depend on inputs from the CADC. The two Air Inlet Control Systems (AICS) are independent isolated computers that control the inlet ramps as a function of airspeed for each engine independently.

*0 to 30 units on the Angle of Attack gauge is equivalent to - 10 to + 40 degrees.

The displays themselves are computers. The VDI and HUD are collectively called the Vertical Display Indicator Group (VDIG). The Horizontal Situation Display (HSD) and the Electronic Counter Measures Display (ECMD) are together called the MDIG for Multipurpose Display Indicator Group. These two groups are capable of displaying separate information to pilot and NFO or showing the same information in both the front and back seat.

The AWG-15 is the computer that actually fires the missiles. A computer is used to avoid the potential tragedy of a short circuit accidentally firing ordnance.

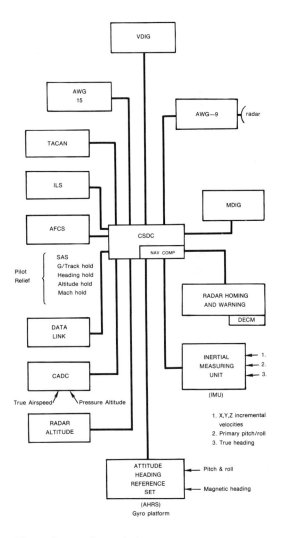

The relationship of the F-14's computers are shown here as all being dependent on the Computer Signal Data Converter. The CSDC integrates all of the computers so that they can talk to each other. Some computers can talk directly to each other without going through the CSDC, however. (Sam Ammons)

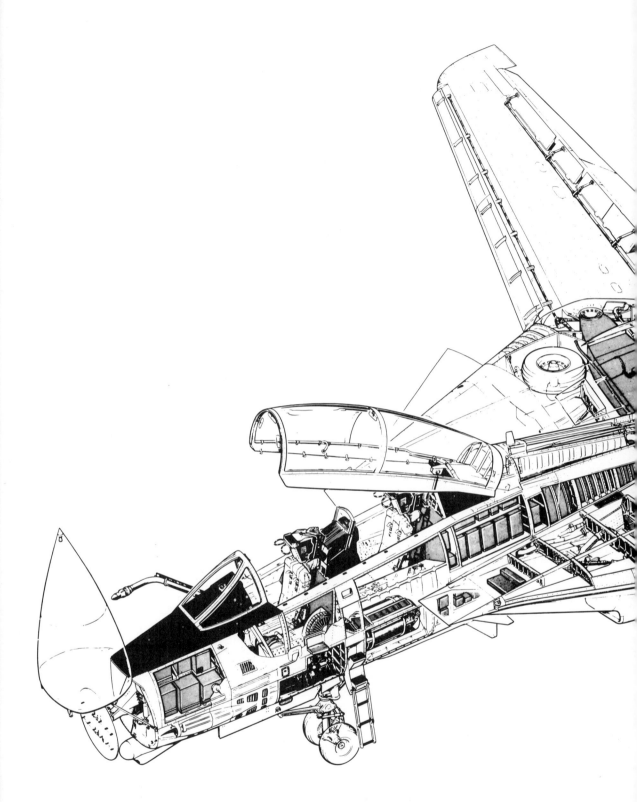

MICHAEL A BADROCKE M.S.I.A
Bethpage-Calverton
1973

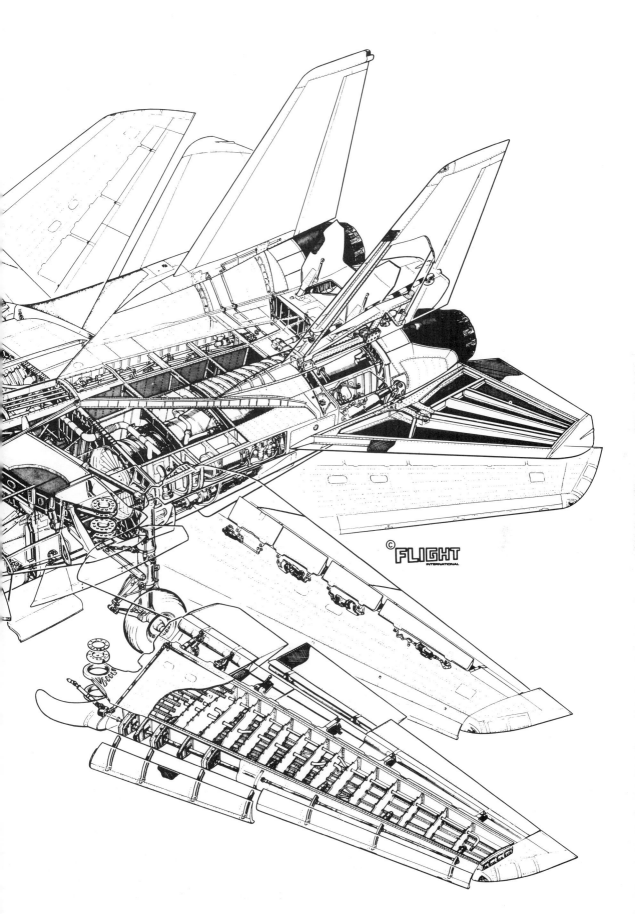

© FLIGHT
INTERNATIONAL

F-14 Cockpit Operations

The two most obvious differences between the F-14's pilot cockpit layout and the cockpit of the F-4 is the F-14's neatness and the two rectangular screens in the middle of the panel. The upper Vertical Display Indicator (VDI) is a TV Raster tube which projects the following information: data link vectoring, automatic carrier landing, aircraft flight attitude, navigation, initiation of visual identification, and attack and target information used during medium and long range missile attacks. The HUD projected on the windscreen is used for visual identification, close in attack situations, final approaches, automatic carrier landings, and the air-to-ground attack.

The lower display, the Horizontal Situation Display (HSD) is the pilot's primary navigation display. The HSD has provisions to display infrared data (IR), electronic counter-measure information, or information from the Tactical Information Display (TID).

The vertically read tape engine instruments are an improvement over the F-4's dial instrument. The F-14 has longer endurance, so comfort is necessary to delay fatigue. The F-14 seat is very comfortable, and even includes vented seats. The NFO's cockpit will be discussed in the Weapons System section.

fuel in military power; however, the engine is less efficient in afterburner than turbojet engines of the same vintage. The TF30 weighs approximately 3,900 pounds and is in the 20,000 pound thrust class. This gives the engine a thrust to weight ratio of over 5:1.

The F-14B was planned to have the Pratt and Whitney F401-PW-400 engine. This is the Navy version of the Advanced Technology Engine (ATE) that was a joint venture with the U.S. Air Force. It was out of this ATE program that the F-15 F100 engine developed. The F401 develops 8,000 pounds more thrust to produce 28,000 pounds of thrust. This would add 16,000 pounds of thrust to the F-14A airframe. The takeoff thrust to weight of the F-14A is .74 to 1. With the F401 engine, the thrust to weight jumps over 1 to 1. By comparison the thrust to weight of the F-4J is .75 to 1. The thrust to weight ratio of the F-14A with the TF-30 engine is deceiving however, because the thrust increases as speed increases due to the ram recovery effect. The F-14A develops 28,000 pounds of thrust per engine at .9 Mach at sea level.

What the F401 engine means in terms of endurance and tactics is obvious when comparing the fuel consumptions of the F-14A and B in power settings needed for equal maneuvers.

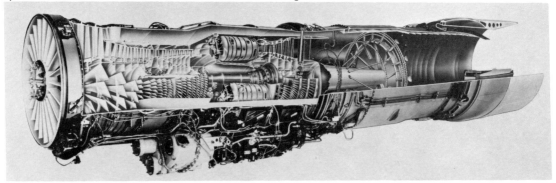

The TF30-P-412 engine develops 20,900 pounds of thrust in zone 5 afterburner at sea level uninstalled. However, at Mach 0.9 at sea level the F-14's turbofan develops 28,000 pounds of thrust in full afterburner.
(Pratt and Whitney Aircraft)

The Pratt and Whitney TF30-P-412A Engine

The TF30-P-412A engine is a dual axial-flow compressor turbofan engine, augmented by five zones of afterburner. It isn't the same engine that was in the F-111B, but it is similar. The basic advantage of the turbofan engine is the lower consumption of

F-14A	F-14B
Zone 3-4 Afterburner (64,000 lbs./hour)	Military (16,000 lbs./hour)
Zone 5 Afterburner (72,000 lbs./hour)	Zone 1 (32,000 lbs./hour)

A VF-1 Tomcat flies over San Diego. Point Loma is in the foreground, Lindbergh Field is in the lower left, and NAS North Island and Coronado are in the center below. The mountains in the distance are Mexico.

(Robert L. Lawson)

F-14 STRUCTURAL COMPONENTS

STEEL   ALUMINUM   TITANIUM   BORON

An F-14 Tomcat in the markings of VF-14.   *(Grumman)*

A VX-4 Test and Evaluation F-14 flies over Southern California.   *(Harry Gann Photo)*

A model of the F-14A Tomcat *with the Imperial Iranian Air Force paint scheme. Iran was the first foreign country to order the F-14. To date they have ordered eighty aircraft.*   *(Grumman)*

An F-14A from the Navy Test Pilot School on the USS Enterprise in June of 1974. This Tomcat was used for Carrier Aligned Inertial Navigation System (CAINS) testing. (Author)

The Tomcat taxies into position for a cat shot with its wings in 75° oversweep. (Author)

A VF-32 Tomcat drives through the stormy East Coast skies. (Grumman)

Tomcat No. 2 is loaded down with everything it can carry. Under the left nacelle is a fuel tank, under the right nacelle is the Mach 1.8 reconnaissance pod. The body tunnel has four Phoenix, and the glove stations one Phoenix each. Also notice the cannards folded down on the nose. (Grumman)

This public relations photo shows the complete set of missiles, ammunitions and ordnance the F-14 can carry, but not all at the same time. (Grumman)

Pilot's Instrument Panel and Consoles

NOTES

⚠1 AIRCRAFT BUNO 158612 THRU 159001

⚠2 AIRCRAFT BUNO 158631 AND SUBSEQUENT AND AIRCRAFT INCORPORATING AFC 35

⚠3 AIRCRAFT BUNO 158978 AND SUBSEQUENT

⚠4 AIRCRAFT BUNO 159002 AND SUBSEQUENT AND AIRCRAFT INCORPORATING AFC 181

⚠5 AIRCRAFT BUNO 159878 AND SUBSEQUENT AND AIRCRAFT INCORPORATING AFC 599

⚠6 AIRCRAFT BUNO 158987 AND SUBSEQUENT AND AIRCRAFT INCORPORATING AFC 529

⚠7 AIRCRAFT BUNO 158978 AND SUBSEQUENT AND AIRCRAFT INCORPORATING AFC 334

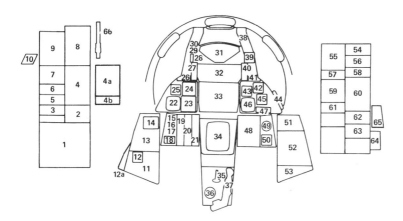

LEFT SIDE CONSOLE
1. G VALVE PUSHBUTTON
2. OXYGEN-VENT AIRFLOW CONTROL PANEL
3. COMM/NAV COMMAND CONTROL PANEL
4. INTEGRATED CONTROL PANEL
4a UHF (AN/ARC 159)
4b UHF COMM SELECT PANEL
5. TONE VOLUME CONTROL PANEL
6. ICS CONTROL PANEL
7. AFCS CONTROL PANEL
8. THROTTLE QUADRANT
9. INLET RAMPS/THROTTLE
   CONTROL PANEL
10. TARGET DESIGNATE SWITCH

LEFT VERTICAL CONSOLE
11. FUEL MANAGEMENT PANEL
12. CONTROL SURFACE POSITION INDICATOR
12a LAUNCH BAR ABORT
13. LANDING GEAR CONTROL PANEL
14. WHEELS-FLAPS POSITION INDICATOR

LEFT KNEE PANEL
15. ENGINE PRESSURE RATIO INDICATOR
16. EXHAUST NOZZLE POSITION INDICATOR
17. OIL PRESSURE INDICATOR
18. HYDRAULIC PRESSURE INDICATOR
19. ELECTRICAL TACHOMETER INDICATOR
    (RPM)
20. THERMOCOUPLE TEMPERATURE
    INDICATOR (TIT)
21. RATE OF FLOW INDICATOR (FF)

LEFT INSTRUMENT PANEL
22. SERVOPNEUMATIC ALTIMETER
23. RADAR ALTIMETER
24. AIRSPEED MACH INDICATOR

25. VERTICAL VELOCITY INDICATOR
26. LEFT ENGINE FUEL SHUTOFF HANDLE
27. ANGLE-OF-ATTACK INDICATOR

LEFT FRONT WINDSHIELD FRAME
28. APPROACH INDEXER
29. WHEELS WARNING LIGHT
29a BRAKES
30. ACLS/AP WARNING LIGHT
30a NWS ENGA

CENTER PANEL
31. HEADS UP DISPLAY
32. AIR COMBAT MANEUVER PANEL
33. VERTICAL DISPLAY INDICATOR (VDI)
34. HORIZONTAL SITUATION DISPLAY
    INDICATOR (HSI)
35. PEDAL ADJUST HANDLE
36. BRAKE PRESSURE INDICATOR
37. CONTROL STICK

RIGHT FRONT WINDSHIELD FRAME
38. ECM WARNING LIGHTS
39. STANDBY COMPASS

RIGHT INSTRUMENT PANEL
40. WING SWEEP INDICATOR
41. RIGHT ENGINE FUEL SHUTOFF HANDLE
42. ACCELEROMETER
43. STANDBY ATTITUDE INDICATOR
44. CANOPY JETTISON HANDLE
45. CLOCK
46. BEARING DISTANCE HEADING
    INDICATOR (BDHI)
47. UHF REMOTE INDICATOR

RIGHT KNEE PANEL
48. FUEL QUANTITY INDICATOR
49. LIQUID OXYGEN QUANTITY INDICATOR
50. CABIN PRESSURE ALTIMETER

RIGHT VERTICAL CONSOLE
51. ARRESTING HOOK PANEL
52. DISPLAYS CONTROL PANEL
53. ELEVATION LEAD PANEL

RIGHT SIDE CONSOLE
54. COMPASS CONTROL PANEL
55. CAUTION—ADVISORY INDICATOR
56. TACAN CONTROL PANEL
57. MASTER GENERATOR CONTROL PANEL
58. ARA-63 CONTROL PANEL
59. AIR CONDITIONING CONTROL PANEL
60. MASTER LIGHT CONTROL PANEL
61. EXTERNAL ENVIRONMENTAL CONTROL
    PANEL.
62. MASTER TEST PANEL
63. HYDRAULIC TRANSFER PUMP SWITCH
64. DEFOG CONTROL LEVER
65. WINDSHIELD DEFOG SWITCH
66. HYDRAULIC HAND PUMP

RIGHT
SIDE
CONSOLE

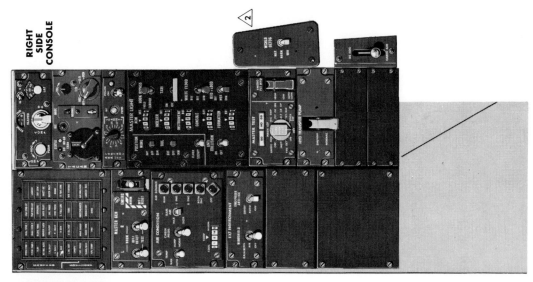

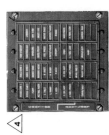

LEFT
SIDE
CONSOLE

HYD HAND PUMP

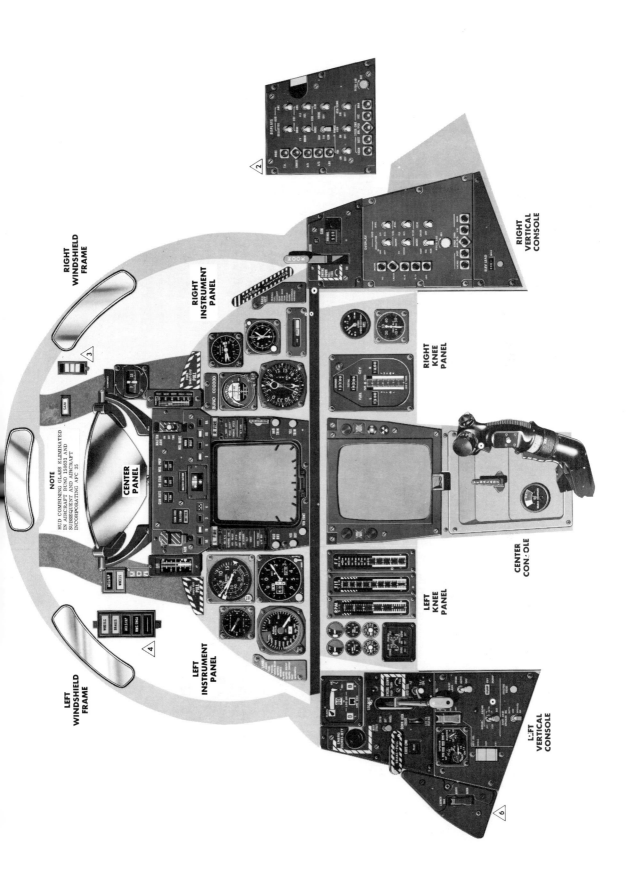

39

NFO Instrument Panel and Consoles

NOTES

△1 AIRCRAFT BUNO 158978 AND SUBSEQUENT

△2 AIRCRAFT BUNO 158612 AND SUBSEQUENT

△3 AIRCRAFT BUNO 158978 AND SUBSEQUENT AND AIRCRAFT INCORPORATING AFC 599

△4 AIRCRAFT BUNO 158978 AND SUBSEQUENT

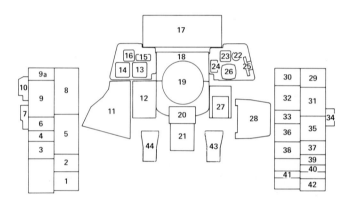

LEFT SIDE CONSOLE
1. G VALVE PUSHBUTTON
2. OXYGEN-VENT AIRFLOW CONTROL PANEL
3. COMM/NAV COMMAND PANEL
4. ICS CONTROL PANEL
5. INTEGRATED CONTROL PANEL
6. TACAN CONTROL PANEL
7. LIQUID COOLING CONTROL PANEL
8. COMPUTER ADDRESS PANEL
9. RADAR IR/TV CONTROL PANEL
9a UHF COMM SELECT PANEL
10. EJECT COMMAND PANEL

LEFT VERTICAL CONSOLE
11. ARMAMENT PANEL

LEFT KNEE PANEL
12. SYSTEM TEST—SYSTEM POWER PANEL

LEFT INSTRUMENT PANEL
13. SERVOPNEUMATIC ALTIMETER
14. AIRSPEED MACH INDICATOR
15. UHF REMOTE INDICATOR
16. STANDBY ATTITUDE INDICATOR

CENTER PANEL
17. DETAIL DATA DISPLAY PANEL (DDD)

CENTER CONSOLE
18. NAVIGATION CONTROL AND DATA READOUT
19. TACTICAL INFORMATION DISPLAY (TID)
20. TACTICAL INFORMATION CONTROL PANEL
21. HAND CONTROL UNIT

RIGHT INSTRUMENT PANEL
22. FUEL QUANTITY TOTALIZER
23. CLOCK
24. THREAT ADVISORY LIGHTS
25. CANOPY JETTISON HANDLE
26. BEARING DISTANCE HEADING INDICATOR (BDHI)

RIGHT KNEE PANEL
27. CAUTION-ADVISORY PANEL

RIGHT VERTICAL CONSOLE
28. MULTIPLE DISPLAY INDICATOR

RIGHT SIDE CONSOLE
29. DIGITAL DATA INDICATOR (DDI)
30. ECM DISPLAY CONTROL PANEL
31. DATA LINK REPLY AND INTERIOR LIGHT CONTROL PANEL
32. ECM CONTROL PANEL
33. DECM CONTROL PANEL
34. DEFOG CONTROL LEVER
35. IFF TRANSPONDER CONTROL PANEL
36. CHAFF/FLARE DISPENSE PANEL
37. AA1 CONTROL PANEL
38. AN/ALE-29A PROGRAMMER
39. IFF ANTENNA ANT AND TEST PANEL
40. RADAR BEACON CONTROL PANEL
41. KY-28 CONTROL PANEL
42. ELECTRICAL POWER SYSTEM TEST PANEL

LEFT AND RIGHT FOOT WELLS
43. MIC FOOT BUTTON
44. ICS FOOT BUTTON

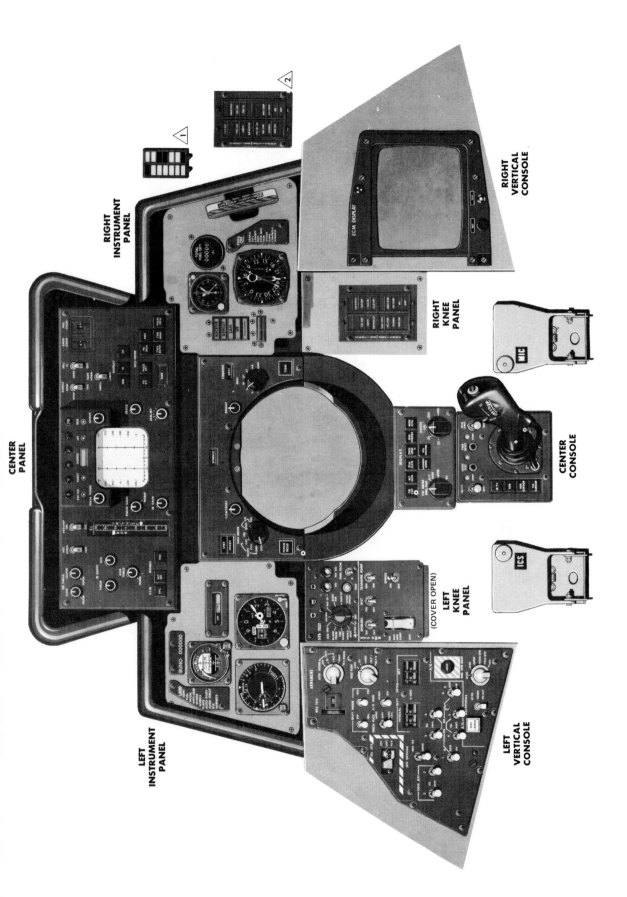

RIGHT SIDE CONSOLE

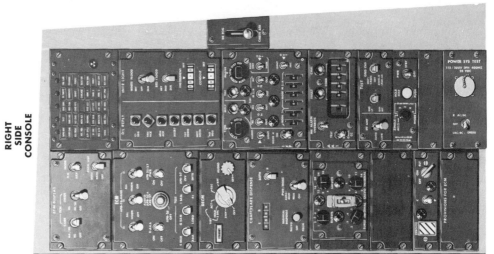

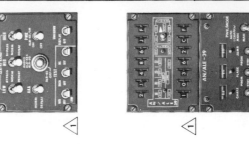

LEFT SIDE CONSOLE

AIRCRAFT DIMENSIONS

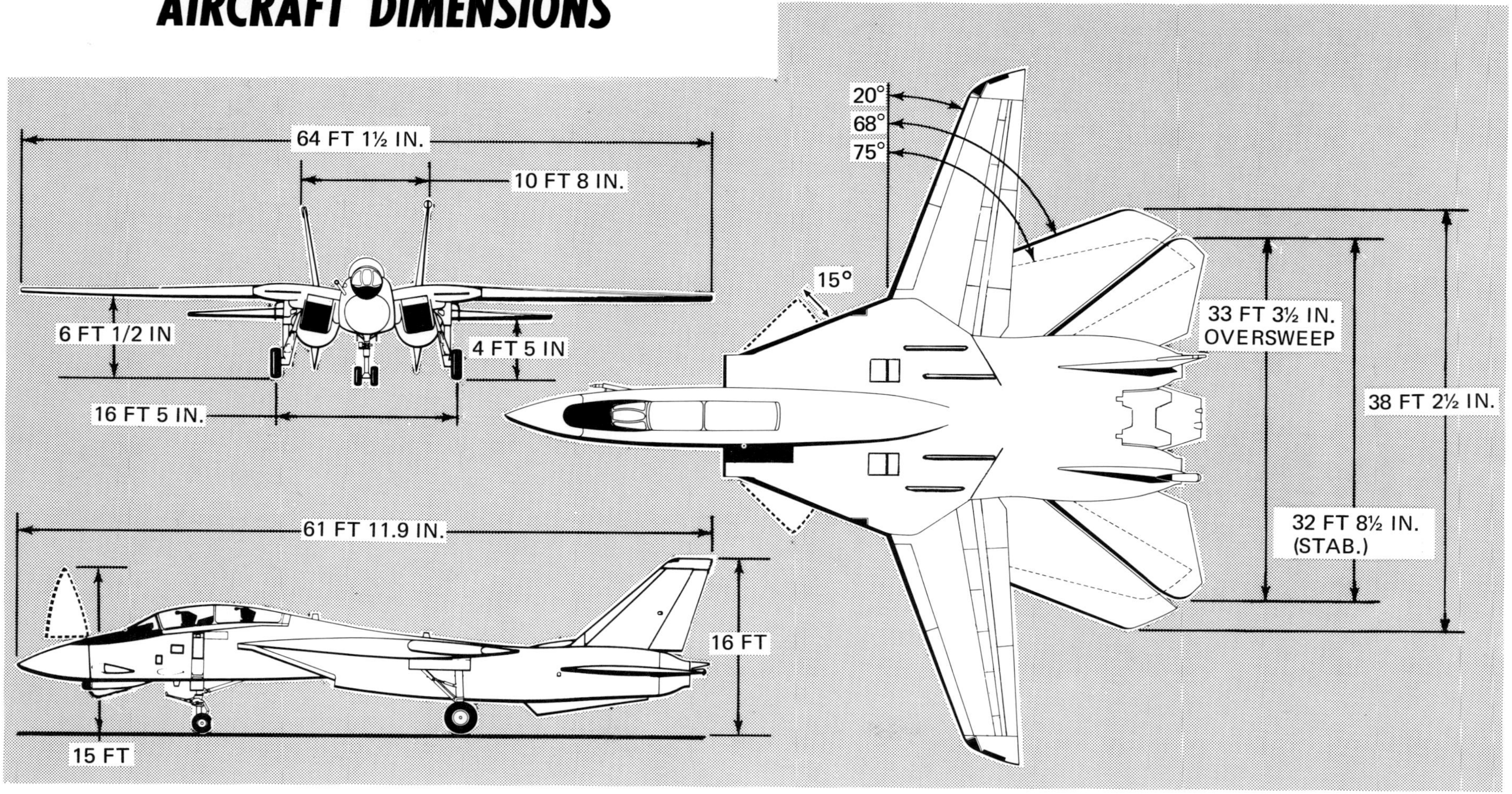

38 FT 2½ IN.

33 FT 3½ IN. OVERSWEEP

32 FT 8½ IN. (STAB.)

20°
68°
75°

15°

10 FT 8 IN.

4 FT 5 IN.

64 FT 1½ IN.

6 FT 1/2 IN

16 FT 5 IN.

16 FT

61 FT 11.9 IN.

15 FT

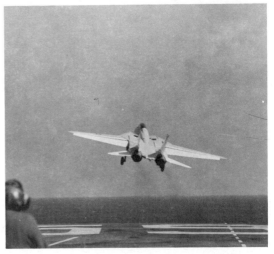

The first F-14 catapult launch takes place June 15th, 1972 from the deck of the USS Forrestal. Notice the stabilator is in the full up position ready to pitch the nose of the F-14 up once flying speed is reached. The pilot is LCDR Emory M. Brown, USN. CDR George W. White, USN, the first Navy pilot to fly the F-14A, is in the back seat. (U.S. Navy)

F-14 Flight Characteristics

What Makes a Good Fighter?

A degree in aeronautical engineering usually helps in understanding a book that talks about aircraft performance. There never seems to be a happy medium — the book is either way over the reader's head, or so simple that it doesn't add to the reader's knowledge. This section of the book gets away from the straight dialogue on the F-14 to try to give the reader an "instant expert" course in some of the principles of aerodynamics.

Deciding what makes a good fighter requires deciding what a fighter should be. Perhaps a definition can act as a starting point. *Fighter* – an aircraft designed primarily to engage at low and medium altitudes in air-to-air combat against other fighters.[24] *Interceptor* — an aircraft that lacks capability to engage and intended primarily for high altitude air-to-air combat against bombers with one shot implications. There is some disagreement as to what a fighter should be. In the McNamara era, the TFX was more bomber than fighter. Some of the confusion might be eliminated if more specific designations were used for the expected role the aircraft will

This is a good example of the thin frontal area the F-14 exposes to the supersonic airstream. Also notice how the cockpit is raised for visibility. This pre-production aircraft does not have the tail modification. The tail nozzles vary in area from 7.5 square feet fully open – as they are here, and as they would be during afterburner – to 3.6 square feet fully closed. A Phoenix missile hangs on the left rear station. Notice the boattail modification. This change was necessary due to cracks that developed in the curved surfaces. (U.S. Navy)

play. An interceptor, then, would be designated with an I, a fighter with an F, and bombers with a B. In the case of multi-role aircraft, both designations could be used as in the FB-111.

The designations even confuse Congress. During a Congressional debate about a new aircraft from the McDonnell Aircraft Company, two senators were arguing about which was the better aircraft — the F-110, an Air Force plane, or the F4H, a Navy plane. Both aircraft were the F-4 *Phantom II* as we

know it today. This embarrassment brought pressure on the Secretary of Defense to make a common designation system for both services. (Readers may draw any conclusions about Congress they like.) Sometimes, for political reasons, the services are forced to call a plane something it isn't. Perhaps it was common knowledge during the development of the F-111 that if it had been called a bomber, it wouldn't have passed the first Congressional sub-committee.

A VF-1 crew check their spoilers before takeoff at NAS Miramar.   (Robert L. Lawson)

To define, then, what makes any aircraft good, we have to define what its mission will be — and then see if it can handle the mission. The mission is influenced by the threat. Since in these days of fiscal restraint, and limited real estate available on aircraft carriers, what makes a good fighter is not really the question since aircraft with the designation "F" for fighter aren't always fighters by our definition. The question is, what makes a good aircraft that has the "F-" designation.

The Navy's requirements dictated the design of the F-14. The need for the stand-off capability never died. The F6D *Missileer* was aborted, the F-111B was killed but the need for the long range fleet defense missile lived on. The threat when the Navy first wanted the *Missileer/Eagle* was the fighter and bomber launched air-to-surface missile. The ship and submarine launched surface-to-surface missile evolved as an additional threat. As a result, the need for the stand-off missile capability became even greater. To these, another requirement was added.

During the middle '60s, the Vietnam War escalated. In November 1966, the MiGs were working with Ground Control Intercept operators (GCI) who were directing the MiGs to the blind spots of our carrier aircraft. The politicians were calling the rules of engagement — the F-4 *Phantoms* were not allowed to operate as designed. Instead of firing their missiles when they made radar contact, the F-4s were required to visually identify their targets. Since the F-4 was designed as an interceptor, and not as an agile dogfighter, the F-4 survived only due to superior training and tactics of the pilot in the ACM environment.

46

A VF-1 Tomcat taking off with the leading edge slats and trailing edge flaps in the take-off mode.
(Robert L. Lawson)

The Navy and Grumman realized that in thinking about the multi-roled VFX, the ACM role — air superiority — must be given more consideration in the deisgn. Grumman designers had the ACM environment in mind when they started work on the F-14. The stand-off missile capability was never forgotten, but this time hopefully the long range platform would be able to dogfight in the sky better than any threat or projected threat through the 1980s. What makes a good fighter is still a legitimate question. A better question to ask is what makes a good air superiority airplane.

A VF-1 Tomcat on final approach to the carrier. Notice the leading edge slats and trailing edge flaps.
(Robert L. Lawson)

An F-14 is launched off the USS Forrestal *during carrier suitability trials, November 26, 1973. Notice the depressed nose strut for the launch.*
(U.S. Navy)

Factors Affecting Air Superiority

There is nothing more important than the skill of the crew, for no airplane can fly itself — at least not yet. Designers have many factors to consider when designing an air superiority aircraft, which will allow the crew's skill to be optimized. Here are some of them.

Relative Aircraft Performance

This includes longitudinal acceleration, or how fast can the plane get from point A to point B in level flight. What is the maximum G the airplane can take? This doesn't mean in a continuous turn, but just how hard can the pilot yank the nose around to fire his guns or missiles. The maximum sustained turning ability is very important. Fuel endurance in combat is very important, because making the other guy run out of gas is tantamount to a kill, as experienced by a North Vietnamese pilot of a MiG-17 shot down by LT Randy Cunningham. Specific excess power describes the ability of an aircraft to climb or accelerate at various G conditions.

Combat Qualities

These are also parameters that the designers can control. They include relative size, engine smoke, flying qualities, field of view and others. They are all important and go into designing an answer to a threat.

Crew Capability and Engagement Conditions

The pilot and NFO's ability depend on their training and individual desire. The engagement conditons, such as initial geometry, sun position, cloud cover, type of terrain are sometimes controllable by the crew, but obviously not always.

In the summer of 1971, then Secretary of Defense David Packard challenged the Director of Development, Research, and Evaluation (DDR&E) of the Department of Defense. He said that the Russian threat may be greater than you estimate. Thus evolved the Navy Fighter Study III. This study was a refined analysis of the threat. It also compared the F-14 with the threat.

One of the techniques used to analyze and compare the F-14 with the threat was a paper — computer-assisted — study called

Air Combat Evaluation plots, or ACE plots. ACE plots compare one airplane against another, and in the dogfight or ACM arena only. Each aircraft is given points for its relative ability. The ACE plots take five parameters of the relative aircraft performance and score them. The aircraft are rated on maximum G available, sustained G available, fuel endurance, time to convert (gain gun firing position) and specific excess power (P_s).[26]

In order to better understand these five parameters, a quick "instant expert" course on lift and drag will help in understanding how these terms relate to fighter performance.

There are four forces that act on a fighter, just like any airplane: lift, weight, drag, and thrust. Thrust makes the plane go forward, lift allows it to climb, drag slows it down, and weight brings it back to earth. Assuming that the thrust is just equal to the drag, the plane will not be accelerating, i.e., it will be flying at a constant airspeed. If the wings can generate enough lift to just equal the weight, then the plane will not be descending or climbing, but flying at a constant altitude. But if more thrust is added to this constant state airplane, the wing will have air molecules rushing across it at a faster speed. This faster speed will allow the wing to generate more lift. The plane will seek a higher altitude where two things will happen to bring the airplane back to a steady state. First, the air molecules will be less dense at the higher altitude which will tend to slow down the lifting effects of this new, faster speed. Secondly, the faster speed will create more drag on the wing. The formula for lift and drag shows how these factors come into effect.

$$L = C_L \ \tfrac{1}{2}\rho V^2 S$$

where C_L = the coefficient of lift (a constant non-dimensional term that is used to compare different wings with each other. C_L is inherent in the design of the wing.)

S = the surface area of the wing

V = the velocity

ρ = the density of the air, i.e., the number of molecules per unit volume.

Looking at the formula, it's easy to see that by increasing either the density, surface area, or speed the lift will increase.

Interestingly enough, the formula for drag looks similar to the formula for lift.

$$D = C_D \ \tfrac{1}{2}\rho V^2 S$$

The terms all mean the same as they did in the lift equations, except that like C_L, C_D is a non-dimension term for drag that is inherent in the design of the airfoil and a function of the angle of attack.

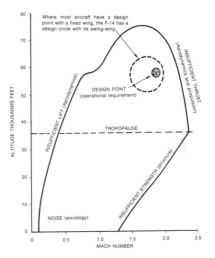

All aircraft have an aerodynamic envelope. This envelope is for a theoretical aircraft, and can be compared to the F-14's envelope to understand what the difference limitations are. Because of the variable-sweep wing, the design point for the wing is enlarged.

These then are the factors that affect lift and drag. However, there are two that haven't been mentioned. The first is the airfoil shape, but the shape is described by the relationship between coefficient of lift or drag (C_L or C_D). The other is angle of attack. The angle of attack is the angle of the wing relative to the local wind coming across it. It is an aerodynamic fact that the greater the angle of attack, the more lift will be generated — up to a point. That point where lift is no longer generated is the angle of attack that results in a stall.

For any given wing, then, we can compare lift qualities and drag qualities by comparing the C_L and C_D because the rest of the factors cancel out.

$$\frac{L}{D} = \frac{C_L \ \tfrac{1}{2}\rho V^2 S}{C_D \ \tfrac{1}{2}\rho V^2 S}$$

However, both C_L and C_D are functions of the angle of attack. The angle of attack, called α (alpha) or AOA, changes, and causes different characteristics in an airfoil. As the AOA is increased, the coefficient of lift increases, but so does the coefficient of drag. They increase at different rates, however. When the ratio of the coefficient of lift, C_L, and the coefficient of drag, C_D is greatest, this point is called L/D_{MAX}. This condition,

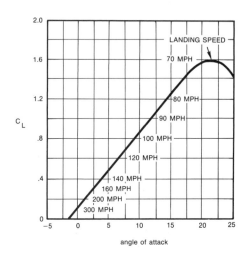

This chart shows in practical terms what happens when an airplane slows down. In order to maintain lift, the angle of attack must increase, to increase the lifting effect of the wing – measured as C_L. (U.S. Air Force)

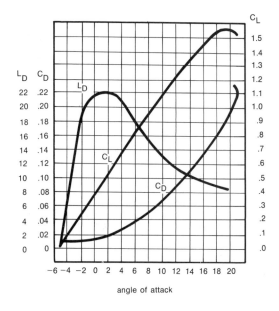

This chart shows a typical set of curves for a given wing section. Notice that L/D max does not give the greatest amount of lift, but the most lift for the least drag. (U.S. Air Force)

L/D_{MAX}, is the condition where the wing's angle of attack gives the greatest amount of lift with the least amount of drag. This L/D_{MAX} condition should never be confused with the greatest amount of lift. The greatest amount of lift occurs just before stalling. There are important characteristics associated with L/D_{MAX} :

> Maximum endurance of jet powered airplanes
> Maximum climb angle for jet powered aircraft
> Maximum power-off glide range for jet airplanes.[27]

Maximum G is the number of times the pull of gravity an airfoil can take before stalling occurs or before a structural limit is

reached. It is sometimes called instantaneous G because most aircraft can only pull maximum G for a quick maneuver before airspeed bleeds off. Thrust and drag are opposite forces in the aerodynamic equation. A high G maneuver creates more drag. The instantaneous G available is a function of C_L only. The C_D only becomes a factor in sustaining the G.

If there isn't enough thrust to overcome this drag at the maximum G the airfoil can produce, the aircraft decelerates or the G is reduced to the amount where engine thrust can sustain the drag created by the lower G or the airplane decelerates. This lower G is called sustained G. Tactically, instananeous G is useful for a quick shot from a gun, short range missile shot, or defensive break turn. Sustained G, however, is given more weight in the ACE evaluations because in a dogfight, the ability to continuously pull or sustain a given G is the measure by which a fighter will continuously out turn the other fighter. Sustained G is a function of C_L (W/S is known as wing loading) where W = weight and S = square footage area of the wing.

$$\frac{C_L}{W/S} \text{ is the same as } \frac{C_L S}{W}$$

so if two airplanes weigh the same, and have the same thrust, and the same airfoil, the airplane with the larger wing area will be able to sustain more Gs and be able to out turn the other.

The two foot by six foot canards on F-14A No. 2 are installed to counteract any spins that develop during the high angle of attack program. The Navy and Marine Corps lost over 200 F-4s to spins and almost 100 pilots. Grumman's goal is a spin-proof airplane. The only spins to date have been from an inverted position, and pilot induced. The F-14 has flown through plus 90° and minus 90° in all center of gravity and wing sweep configurations. The Aileron-Rudder-Interconnect (ARI) allows the pilot to have the same operating and maneuvering envelope – a Navy first. *(Grumman)*

Comparing the G capability of two airplanes at a given altitude and Mach number is really a comparison of their relative aerodynamic capabilities. Talking in terms of G is just a shorthand method for talking about C_L, thrust to weight ratio and various other parameters.

Fuel endurance is almost self-explanatory. The longer an aircraft can stay in the air, the longer the airplane can perform the mission. The ideal fleet defense aircraft would stay up all day. Fuel endurance is important in air superiority too. Running out of gas gives the same result as getting shot down.

Specific excess power (P_S) is a measure of the difference between an airplane's thrust and its drag. Wings create lift, but they also create drag. A small wing reduces the amount of drag, at a given angle of attack, but it also limits the amount of lift the thrust is capable of converting into lift. A large wing creates a lot of lift, but it may create more drag than the engine thrust can overcome. In any configuration, when the thrust available exceeds the drag, the airplane can gain speed or altitude or both. This "excess" thrust is called specific excess power and is measured in feet per second. The formula is expressed:

$$P_S = \frac{(T\text{-}D)V}{W}$$

Where T is thrust

D = drag

W = weight

V = velocity

Tactically, the fighter with greater P_S can out climb or out accelerate or out turn an opponent and convert the excess thrust into an advantage.

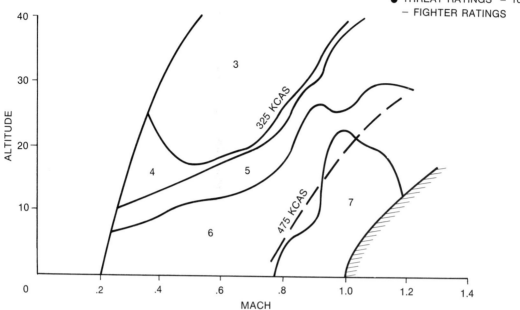

**ACE PILOT
FIGHTER VS. THREAT**

● FIGHTER RATINGS SHOWN
● THREAT RATINGS = 10
  − FIGHTER RATINGS

ACM TACTICS - AIR COMBAT ZONES

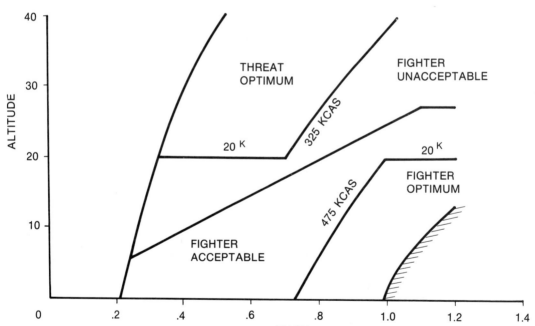

The ACE Plots show the relative ability of two aircraft. Numbers are assigned to various parts of the flight envelope which show the relative ability of our fighter compared to their threat aircraft. The maximum number is 10. Therefore, if you see the number 5 the two aircraft have equal capabilities. The number 7 would indicate our fighter would prevail; the number 3 would indicate their threat aircraft would win the dogfight.

The chart below has taken the data from above, and put it in simpler form to read by calling out Air Combat Zones. On the next page another chart depicts the various maneuvers recommended for the fighter to use against the threat aircraft in these same zones within the flight envelope.   (Flight Systems, Inc.)

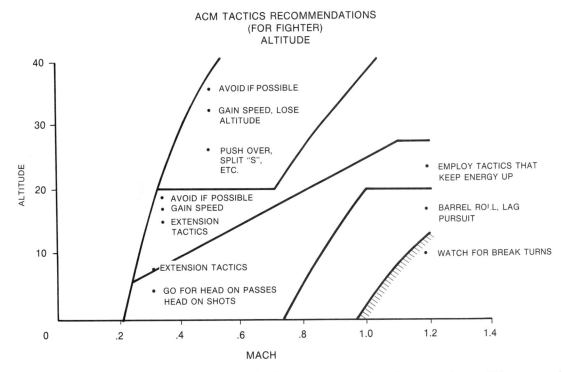

ACM TACTICS RECOMMENDATIONS
(FOR FIGHTER)
ALTITUDE

- AVOID IF POSSIBLE
- GAIN SPEED, LOSE ALTITUDE
- PUSH OVER, SPLIT "S", ETC.
- AVOID IF POSSIBLE
- GAIN SPEED
- EXTENSION TACTICS
- EXTENSION TACTICS
- GO FOR HEAD ON PASSES HEAD ON SHOTS
- EMPLOY TACTICS THAT KEEP ENERGY UP
- BARREL ROLL, LAG PURSUIT
- WATCH FOR BREAK TURNS

Each of the five parameters is weighed according to its relative importance. An example would be instantaneous G compared with sustained G. Obviously the ability to snap the nose around a turn is less valuable than the ability to sustain a turn. Each of the categories is evaluated for the two airplanes being compared. After each of the five categories is compared, the airplanes are compared on a chart. The scoring system is subjective, based on computer data and pilot experience. The scoring system goes like this: If one aircraft receives a maximum of ten points, then the other gets 0. If one receives five, then the other receives five. Once all the points are compared and awarded, they are summarized on a chart. The chart shows altitude versus Mach and the various areas within the flight envelope where each aircraft has advantages over the other. These advantages are not singled out for any one of the five parameters, but summarize all of them.

The ACE plots contained within the Navy Fighter Study III are a method of showing the relative capability of two aircraft. An ACE plot comparing the F-14 to the F-4 would immediately show the superiority of the F-14 over the F-4. Also contained within that same study are charts showing comparisons of sustained G, Instantaneous G, and P_s for the F-14 and F-4.

The F-14 has features that will let it excel in the four areas that are used in the ACE plot studies. The F-14 has demonstrated 9 positive Gs and 5 and ½ negative Gs. The design specifications called for 7.33 positive Gs. Part of the reason for the ability to withstand high G is the high percentage of titanium in the aircraft.

The high sustained G ability of the F-14 is a function of the low wing loading and the variable sweep wing. The aerodynamics of the swing wing allow it to search through its sweep limits for the maximum lift. The program in the CADC's Mach Sweep Programmer was originally programmed for C_L Max in the first 22 F-14s. This put more bending moment in the wings than the Navy wanted, so the program was rewritten so that the wing's position gives the F-14 maximum P_s.

Time to convert is also a function of the swing wing. The straight wing effect lets the F-14 turn more dramatically without losing energy. Fuel endurance is a function of both the turbofan engine and the low induced drag of the wing in the unswept loiter position.

The F-14 has combined all the elements identified by the ACE plots to make it a superior fighter. One feature that seems to affect all of the ACE plot parameters is the variable sweep wing.

53

Why the Swing Wing

One reason for the swing wing seems intuitively simple for some: it lets the airplane go faster by swinging resistance out of the way. It's the same reasoning that a child develops when he rides with his hand out the car window. When he sticks his arm straight out the side of the window (at right angles to the direction the car is traveling), he feels greater resistance than when he lets his arm swing back.

However intuitive this seems, it isn't the total reason for the swing wing. There are two major types of drag. The type that the young child experiences is called parasite drag. Parasite drag, sometimes called the "barndoor effect," increases as the speed

anticipation of riding over the top of the wing causes the relative wind to come in from a higher angle than when it was further out in the remote free airstream. The wing has to increase its angle of attack to get the relative wind coming straight across it. This increased angle tips the lifting force back slightly. The difference between the total lift on the wing and the effective lift force (that lift perpendicular to the relative wind) is the induced drag.

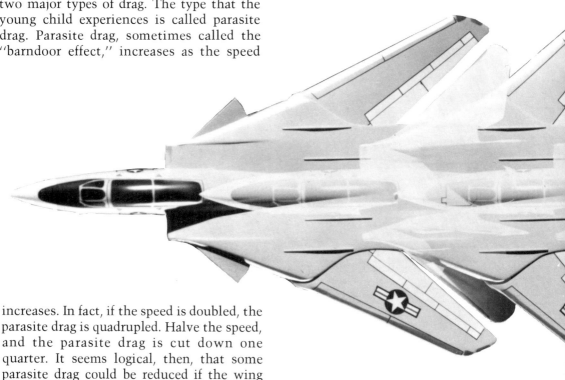

increases. In fact, if the speed is doubled, the parasite drag is quadrupled. Halve the speed, and the parasite drag is cut down one quarter. It seems logical, then, that some parasite drag could be reduced if the wing were swept, and indeed it does.

Induced drag is the other form of drag that contributes to the total drag equation. Induced drag is associated with lift. A wing going through the air disrupts the status quo, just as a rock does when thrown into a pond of still water. The air molecules sense that something is coming at them. They anticipate that they are going to run over the top of a wing. The definition of lift is a force perpendicular and upward from the remote free airstream. The remote free airstream is that undisturbed air off in the distance ahead of the wing. Induced drag is not created by the remote airstream. The airstream that induces drag is that local airstream which anticipates arriving over the wing. This

There is a positive pressure on the underside of the wing. There is also a negative pressure on the upper surface of the wing. Since the pressure is greater under the wing, it tries to fill the area of less pressure on top. It does this by sliding around and over the tip of the wing. In doing this, it creates vortices. This tip vortex combines with the anticipated relative wind and further aggravates induced drag.

There are several additional terms necessary in understanding the full implication of the swing wing. The wing span, b, is roughly the distance from the fuselage to the tip. The wing cord, c, is the average distance from the leading edge to the trailing edge of the wing. The wing area, S, is simply the number of square feet, i.e., for a rectangular wing the wing span, b, times the wing cord, c, S = bxc. An important term, Aspect Ratio, AR, is the ratio of the span, b, to the average chord c, AR = b/c. Aspect Ratio is important because the higher the aspect ratio, the lower the induced drag. If two wings have exactly the same area, they

mentioned previously, induced drag is partly a function of wing tip vortices disrupting the flow at the end of the wing. Ideally, then, the further away from the lifting part of the wing the disruption occurs, the better. When the tip vortices are closer, as they are in a low aspect ratio wing, they are pro-

do not necessarily contribute the same amount of lift. The Aspect Ratio plays a part. The wing that is short and stubby, i.e., low aspect ratio, will create more induced drag than the wing that is long and slender, the high aspect ratio wing. Another way to say this is that if two wings have equal area, and are creating equal lift, then the wing with the lower Aspect Ratio must necessarily be at a higher angle of attack. As

portionally bigger with respect to the lifting area of the wing. The closer vortex creates a greater disturbance in the downwash, and requires the wing to take a larger bite of the air, due to a shift in the relative wind. This larger bite creates larger tip vortices and so on it goes. While in level flight parasite drag increases with higher

This frontal view of the F-14 shows some of the features that give it its unique aerodynamic qualities. The twin vertical tails and dorsal ventral fins give it longitudinal stability. The high mounted cockpit gives excellent visibility and the narrow frontal area eliminates much of the supersonic drag. (Flight International)

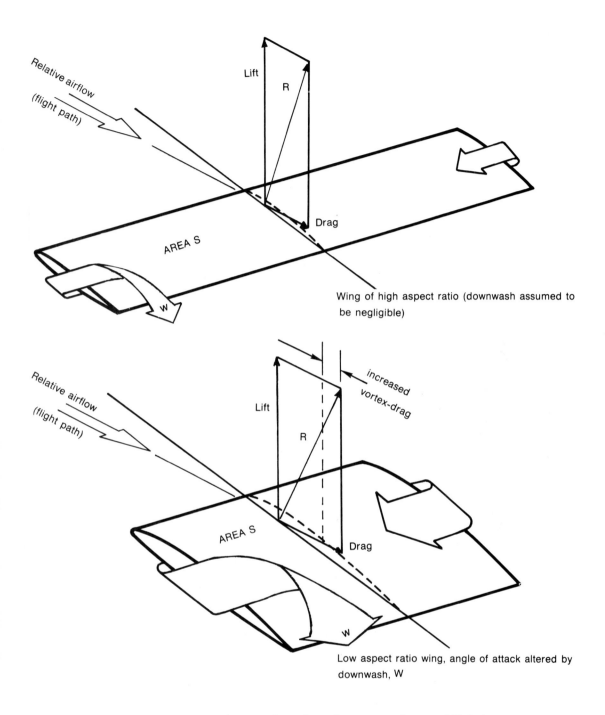

Relative airflow
(flight path)

Lift

R

Drag

AREA S

W

Wing of high aspect ratio (downwash assumed to
be negligible)

Relative airflow
(flight path)

Lift

increased
vortex-drag

R

AREA S

Drag

W

Low aspect ratio wing, angle of attack altered by
downwash, W

The effect of aspect ratio upon wings of equal area generating equal lift (note
increased attitude of low aspect ratio wing to flight path)

The Aspect Ratio of a wing has a lot to do with the performance of the aircraft. If two aircraft have a wing with the same area, but different Aspect Ratios as in the illustration above, there will be greater vorticies generated as well as more induced drag by the wing with the lower Aspect Ratio. Since the air underneath the wing is constantly trying to get to an area of lower pressure, the further away the tip is from the mean area of the wing, the less influence the tip vorticies can have on induced drag.

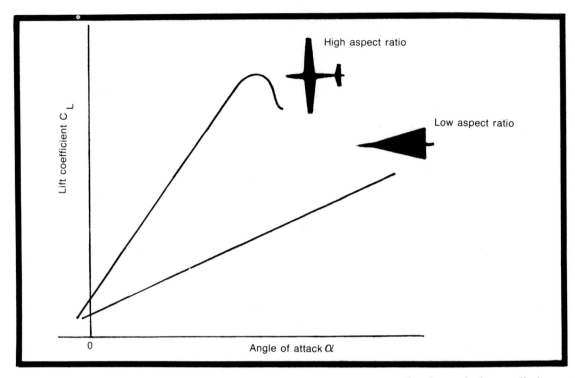

High aspect ratio

Low aspect ratio

Lift coefficient C_L

0

Angle of attack α

A high Aspect Ratio wing gives more lift for a given amount of angle of attack, but stalls long before a low Aspect Ratio wing reaches its lifting limit.

speed, induced drag decreases. On the other hand, parasite drag falls off as speeds lower, while induced drag increases. Induced drag increases because at lower speed, the AOA must be increased to maintain the same lift. Induced drag is one of the killers in the approach and landing pattern.

In the landing pattern, then, we can see one of the benefits of the F-14 swing wing. With the wings swept back, the Aspect Ratio would be low, and induced drag would be high. To land in this configuration would require the high angle of attack, and the high sink rates that can be developed with delta wing aircraft. (The F-14 can land with the wings back, but has a landing speed of 145 knots and a landing roll of 4,500 feet compared with its normal 1,000 to 1,500 foot rollout.) The F-14's CADC sweeps the wings forward, thus making the induced drag less, and lets the F-14 land about 115 knots. By contrast the F-4 lands about 140 knots.

The variable sweep wing allows the pilot — through the computer — to redesign the airplane in the air. The F-14 has three main jobs, Air Superiority, Fleet Air Defense (now called Fleet Air Superiority) and air to ground or attack. These different missions require different aerodynamic designs, and

explain the need for the variable sweep wing.

The swept wing was first introduced in the 1940's as a method to postpone drag rise by delaying (as a function of speed) the beginning of compressibility effects. This is the principal reason for the swept wings that are on all high speed airliners and military airplanes. The swept wing has some disadvantages too. The tip of the wing tends to stall first. If the aileron is out there, as it usually is, there will be a loss of lateral control. The F-14 doesn't use ailerons, but uses a differential tail. The amount of lift available is reduced at subsonic speeds in a swept wing, when compared to an unswept wing of the same aspect ratio. There are associated increases in stall, takeoff, and landing speeds. The structural complications require that more weight for more strength is added to build a swept wing.

Although this is not the full story on the swept wing, it does give an indication of some of the benefits and problems. It should become clearer that by redesigning the wing in flight, the F-14 can take advantage of the characteristics of both the swept and straight wing. A fixed wing is designed to be most efficient at a specific point in the flight

A Tomcat *from VF-1 climbs over San Clemente Island. Easily seen are the indentations in the body for the four* Sparrow *missiles.* *(Robert L. Lawson)*

Straight Wing 0°	Swept Wing 70°
•High lift at low angle of attack (AOA)	•High lift at higher AOA
•Abrupt loss of lift (stall) at moderate AOA	•No abrupt loss of lift at very high AOA
•High lift/drag at low AOA	•Low lift/drag at higher AOA
•Low drag at $L/D_{MAX.}$, therefore low thrust required	•Higher drag at $L/D_{MAX.}$, therefore higher thrust required
•High sustained and instantaneous turn performance-stall limited	•Lower sustained, higher instantaneous turn performance, thrust limited
•High drag (parasite) at high speed	•Low drag (parasite) at high speed
•Low stall speed-aerodynamically limited	•Very low speed-thrust and control limited

envelope. Any place else the airplane flies, must necessarily be a compromise from this wing-speed-altitude point.

While the F-14's wing is designed to be an all-envelope continuous operating wing, the Soviet built variable sweep fighters used the swing wing essentially for take-off and landing only. The F-14's Mach Sweep Programmer (MSP) sweeps the wing from 7 and 1/2° per second at 1 G to better than 4° per second at 7 and 1/2 Gs. The F-111B, by contrast, could sweep its wing manually at 3 and 1/2 degrees per second at 1 G. The F-111B's wing wouldn't sweep under G loading.

To summarize the advantages of the swing wing, we can compare two theoretical airplanes. These two hypothetical airplanes with wing span, aspect ratios, fineness ratios, (ratio of thickness to chord) and basic aerodynamic characteristics equal, differ only in the sweep angle of their wings.

These characteristics, broken down into operational capabilities for a fighter airplane, dictate that for low landing speed, maximum range and endurance, high

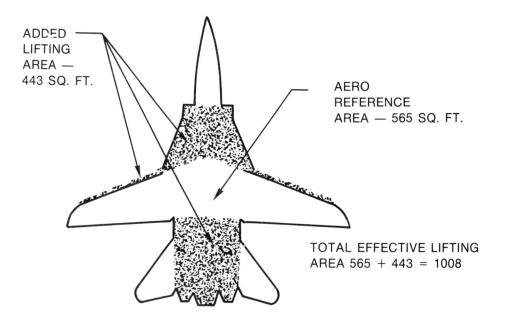

ADDED LIFTING AREA — 443 SQ. FT.

AERO REFERENCE AREA — 565 SQ. FT.

TOTAL EFFECTIVE LIFTING AREA 565 + 443 = 1008

The wing area isn't the only lifting device on the F-14. (Grumman)

sustained turn performance, a straight wing is preferred. For maximum speed and acceleration, and low drag at transonic and supersonic speeds, the highly swept (low drag) wing is preferable. The solution is to develop a wing that may be optimized throughout the operating envelope of the airplane.[28]

Other Flight Characteristics of the F-14

Wing loading is an important characteristic for agile fighters. Wing loading is the weight of the aircraft divided by the square footage of the wing.

W/S where S = wing span (b) x cord (c)

A glider is an example of a very low wing loaded aircraft. The low wing loading plus high L/D is what allows it to almost float. Low wing loading also contributes to a short turn radius. The lift over drag ratio best explains this greater ability to turn with a low wing loaded airplane. When the lift over drag ratio is at a maximum (L/D_{MAX}) the lift minus drag is at a maximum. Since the wing

is what normally provides the lift, the greater the wing area, the greater the lift. Naturally the drag goes up. However, in a variable sweep wing, the drag goes up slower than in a fixed wing. Lowering the wing loading increases an airplane's ability to pull sustained Gs, because the plane can get greater lift at a lower angle of attack which is an advantage because at lower angles of attack, the wing creates less induced drag. Low wing loaded airplanes also have more instantaneous G available, assuming no structural limitation.

In the F-14 the wing is not the only lift generator. The wing area as we normally think of it contributes 565 square feet. However, the area between the nacelles — the wing glove, leading edge slats, and maneuvering flaps — contribute 443 square feet for a total of 1008 square feet. If the area of just the wing is used (565 square feet), the wing loading of the F-14 is greater than the F-4J. In that case the F-14's wing loading would be 97 pounds per square foot, while the F-4J's wing loading is 77.8 pounds per square foot.[29] The actual wing loading is 44 pounds per square foot at 20 degrees and 48

A VF-1 pilot takes some gas while he checks his fuel probe. (Robert L. Lawson)

pounds per square foot at 68 degrees.* The MiG-21J, as a point of comparison, has a wing loading of 65 pounds per square foot. The shape of the F-14 lets it act as a lifting body. In fact, the lift from the wings tends to stop about 10 degrees angle of attack, while the lift from the body increases up to 35 degrees angle of attack, where the maximum lift coefficient (C_L MAX.) is reached.[30] Looking at the F-14 from the top it is obvious that there is a lot of surface area to help provide lift. However, facing the front of the F-14, or looking at it from behind, there is a minimal amount of cross sectional frontal area. (An increase in frontal area creates supersonic drag. The F-111B had 56 square feet of cross sectional frontal area, while the F-14 has only 43 square feet.)

Another large factor in fighter performance is aircraft thrust to weight (T.W.). The ratio of thrust to weight is important in acceleration. No single factor, as you can gather by now, tells the entire

story of performance, but if two airplanes have all other aerodynamic factors equal, the aircraft with the greater thrust to weight will prevail if both pilots have equal ability. Thrust to weight is simply the thrust in pounds divided by the weight in pounds.

$$\frac{T \ (\text{thrust})}{W \ (\text{weight})}$$

An F-4J with two 17,900 pound thrust engines give it a .75 T.W. ratio when it weighs 47,000 pounds. An F-14A with full fuel and four Sparrow missiles weighs approximately 57,000 pounds. The thrust available is 41,800 pounds from the two TF30-P-412A engines. The T.W. ratio is .74 on takeoff, which is less than the *Phantom.* Remember, however, that the thrust in the F-14's engines gets as high as 28,000 pounds. Compare, again, the acceleration of the F-14 to the F-4J. From .8 Mach to 1.8 Mach the F-14 can accelerate 60 per cent faster than the F-4. The F-4J can accelerate slightly better than 50 per cent faster than the F-111B which took over 6 minutes to accelerate from .8 to 1.8 Mach.

*The Navy uses 60% fuel and combat stores (gun, ammo and 4 Sparrow missiles) to compute weight for the wing loading solution.

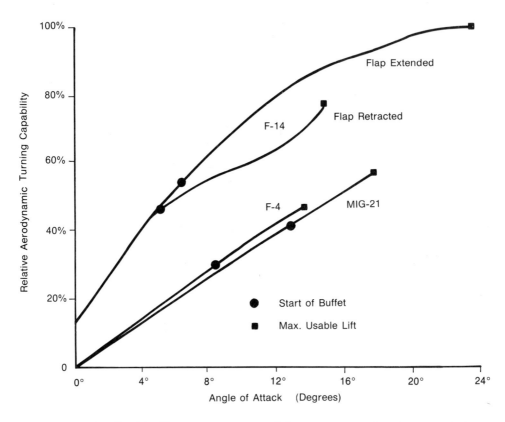

F-14 Maneuver slat/flap lift effects on turning capability as compared to the F-4 and the MiG-21.

(Grumman)

How Good a Fighter is the F-14?

With all this background on what makes a good fighter, we can now make an intelligent comparison to find out how good a fighter the F-14 really is. There are several ways to compare one fighter to another. The F-4 will be our point of comparison for the F-14, with threat aircraft mentioned whenever possible. The ACE plot is one way to compare. An actual fight with the two aircraft pitted against each other would be a truer test. The pilots should be of equal ability to isolate the plane's ability. This section will show some comparisons in terms of performance and raw data that the reader can compare with the F-4 to draw his own conclusions.

F-14/F-4 Comparison

The F-14 has these percentage improvements over the F-4.
- 40% better turn radius
- 27% better maneuvering climb
- 21% better sustained G
- 21% better acceleration
- 20% better rate of climb

- 21% better roll performance
- 80% more combat radius on internal fuel
- 50% more loiter time with 6 Phoenix missiles*
- 100% more loiter time with 4 Sparrow missiles
- More than twice the radar range
- More than 2 and 1/2 times the missile range

Several F-14 crews have given testimony to the fact that a section (2 aircraft) can outfight eight F-4 *Phantoms*. Comparing the assets that means the two F-14s are using four crewmen as opposed to the sixteen necessary for the eight F-4s.

CDR Jim Taylor, CO of VF-2, talks about the impressive performance of the F-14. It was CDR Taylor along with his NFO then LT Kurt Strauss who dazzled the aeronautical world with their performance at the Paris Airshow in May of 1973. Quoting Taylor in 1973 captures the flavor of the F-14's ability.

No matter what other fighters you put against us, we are going to come out on top in a turning dogfight. At 30 degrees

*Compared with Sparrow-equipped F-4.

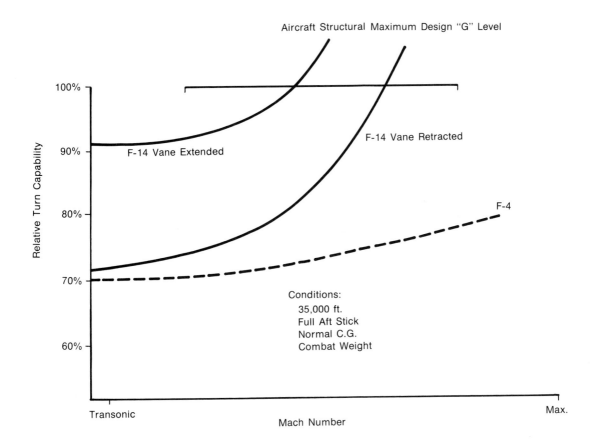

Aircraft Structural Maximum Design "G" Level

F-14 Vane Extended

F-14 Vane Retracted

F-4

Relative Turn Capability

100%

90%

80%

70%

60%

Conditions:
35,000 ft.
Full Aft Stick
Normal C.G.
Combat Weight

Transonic

Mach Number

Max.

Effect of glove vane on supersonic maneuvering of the F-14 compared to the F-4.   *(Grumman)*

angle-of-attack, the F-4 is out of control but Tomcat's still gun-tracking the target smoothly.

If you "trap" another fighter in your six (at the six-o'clock position dead astern), he is actually trapped there. You can generally maneuver him out in front and be tracking him in 30 or 40 seconds. If the other guy is exceptionally good, it might take five or six vertical rolling scissor maneuvers – say three minutes, maximum – to put him in front where you've got him. That would be the longest dogfight I can imagine in the F-14.

If the F-14 passes another fighter head-on – and let's say the other one is flown by the "super number one ace of the base" – he better not turn to meet us. He better just keep right on going the same direction he is headed. If he does turn, he's between a rock and a hard place. He'll become a grape and we'll just eat him up. I'm not joking, it's true.

What other airplane can pull 4-4.5 g's and still be under full control when the wings are stalled? What other fighter is controllable at 100 or 110 knots? Most development aircraft are just sweating to meet their specifications, while the F-14 is exceeding the spec in a lot of areas.[31]

The United States' first ace in Vietnam, Navy pilot LT Randy Cunningham, gives his impressions of the F-14:

What you need is superior thrust response – the instant high speed – when you want it, coupled with uncanny maneuverability. That is what those big turbofans and the flight-programmed swing wing give the F-14. The F-4 can't touch the F-14 in that category – nor can any other fighter including the MiG-23.[32]

One of the fears that fighter pilots live with is approaching the flying limits of the airplane. Unlike the Cessna 150 which gives plenty of warning before a stall, and doesn't do much when it does, the F-4 Phantom gives little warning. When the F-4 does stall,

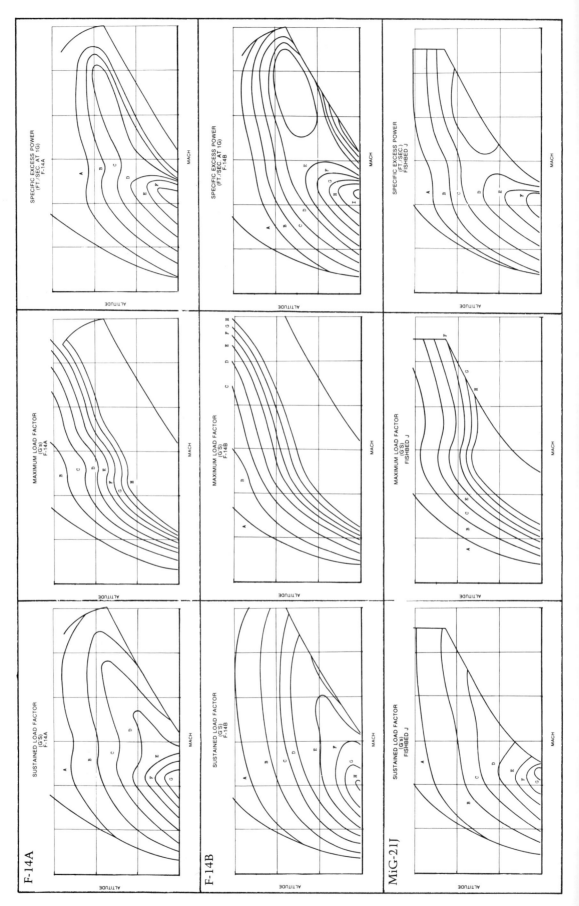

F-14A

SUSTAINED LOAD FACTOR
(G'S)
F-14A

MAXIMUM LOAD FACTOR
(G'S)
F-14A

SPECIFIC EXCESS POWER
(FT./SEC. AT 1G)
F-14A

F-14B

SUSTAINED LOAD FACTOR
(G'S)
F-14B

MAXIMUM LOAD FACTOR
(G'S)
F-14B

SPECIFIC EXCESS POWER
(FT./SEC. AT 1G)
F-14B

MiG-21J

SUSTAINED LOAD FACTOR
(G'S)
FISHBED J

MAXIMUM LOAD FACTOR
(G'S)
FISHBED J

SPECIFIC EXCESS POWER
(FT./SEC.)
FISHBED J

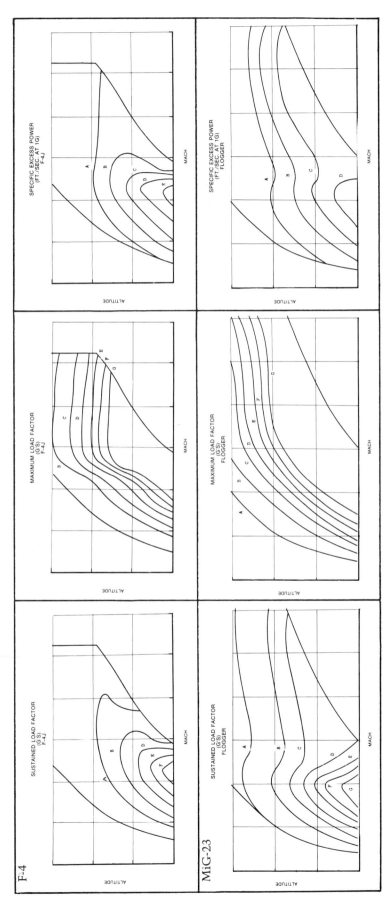

These charts show the relative performance of the F-14A with other aircraft in Maximum (Instantaneous) G, Sustained G, and Specific Excess Power (Ps). The outer line represents the flight envelope of these aircraft. By comparing the density of the areas within these flight envelopes you can tell what kind of performance these aircraft will have at a given altitude and Mach number. (The altitude and Mach number have been intentionally omitted.) By comparing the F-14A with the F-14B, for example, it is simple to see what a difference the F401 engine would make.

The MiG-21 and the MiG-23 are the two current threat aircraft that the F-14A and F-14B were designed to counter. (The F-14 was originally going to have the A engine (TF30-P-412A) in the first 86 aircraft and the B engine (F401-PW-400) in the rest of the production line, the first 86 being retrofitted with the B engine at a later date.) To find out which aircraft would have the greater climb capability (at 1 G) compare two aircraft at the same intersection of Mach number and altitude on the Ps chart. The same comparison can be made for the relative turning capability on the Instantaneous (Maximum) G and Sustained G charts. Compare the F-14s and MiG-21 and MiG-23, both swing wing aircraft with the F-4 and MiG-23, which are fixed wing.

General Arrangement

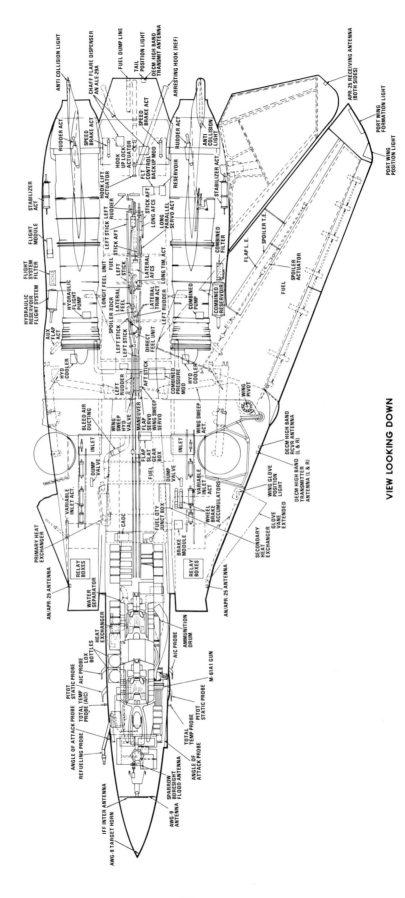

VIEW LOOKING DOWN

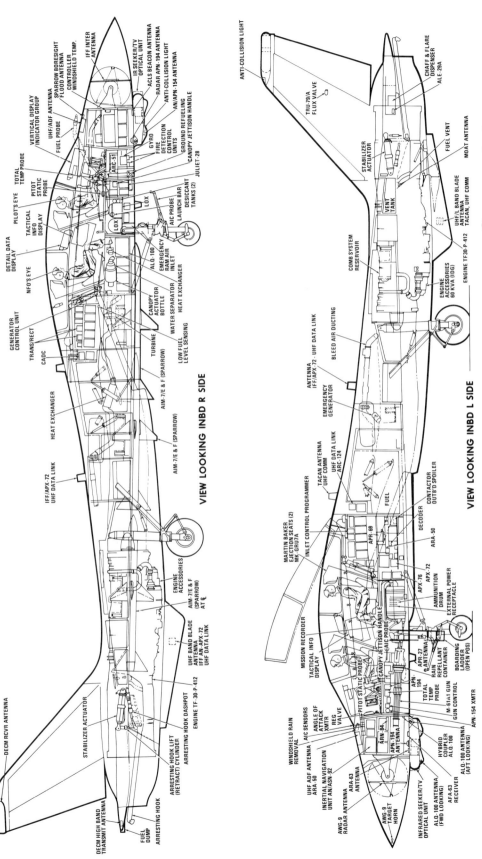

General Arrangement

VIEW LOOKING INBD R SIDE

VIEW LOOKING INBD L SIDE

67

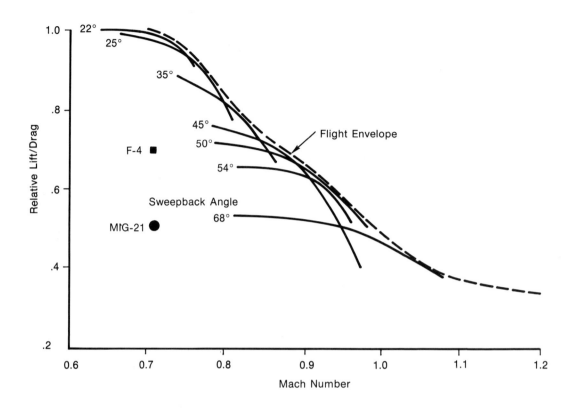

F-14 flight envelope life/drag versus speed. (Grumman)

it's usually lightning fast and likely to end up in a spin. There have been over 200 F-4s crash from spin related incidents. While the Cessna 150 pilot is practicing how to fly straight and level, and to avoid maneuvers that approach the dangerous edges of the Cessna's limits, the fighter pilot is pushed closer and closer to recognizing just how close he can fly to the aerodynamic brink before his plane departs. The Grumman engineers designed the F-14 to allow a neophyte Ensign aviator to fly the F-14 beyond what would be the edges of controllability for the F-4. In fact, the new F-14 pilot is introduced to flying right up to the edges of the maneuvering and performance envelope of the F-14 at the beginning of his training. Normally this type of training would come late in the training syllabus, and after the seasoned aviator could recognize when he was approaching trouble.

This lack of fear of the F-14 helps create more aggressive pilots, which is a most necessary ingredient. The ability to fly at 25 degrees angle of attack at 50 knots, and still be able to roll 360 degrees would instill confidence in any pilot.[33]

The F-14 has been as fast as Mach 2.6 and as slow as zero airspeed, still completely controllable. The rate of sink at zero airspeed, 9,000 feet per minute. In an effort to increase the maneuvering envelope, the Navy and Grumman initiated some structural qualification tests.

In tests to date, the structural aircraft has attained 9.0g at 1.2 Mach, 20,000 feet, 8.0g at .90 Mach, 20,000 feet with 6 AIM-54 Phoenix Missiles, 2 — 267 gallon drop tanks and 2 AIM-9G Sidewinders installed, and attained over 7g at Mach 2.04 at 50,000 feet with all loads well within limit strength capability.[34]

The F-14 has pulled over 6.5g, at speed below 275 knots.

A VX-4 Test and Evaluation squadron F-14 gets a drive from an A-3 "Whale." Insert shows an F-14 taking a drink from an A-7 somewhere in the Indian Ocean during the F-14's first Western Pacific deployment (Harry Gann Photo/U.S. Navy)

(Steve Miller)

An F-14 from VF-1 prepares to catch a number three wire during the carrier qualification in June 1974. (Author)

An F-14 Tomcat from VF-1 prepares for a launch. This series depicts the series of maneuvers to prepare for flying at 130 knots after a 120 foot flight down the catapult track. Notice in the last picture how the stabilators are deflected to pitch the nose up at the end of the catapult. (Author)

An F-14 from VF-1 approaches with hook down during carrier qualifications in June, 1974. (Author)

The F-14B in flight testing the Pratt & Whitney F401-PW-400 engine. The F-401 engine will give the F-14 about 16,000 additional pounds of thrust. *(Grumman)*

Portrait of a VF-1 Tomcat *crew.* (Author)

Before and After: This series shows the different paint schemes for VF-1 and VF-2. Under its first commanding officer, CDR Sam Leeds, the VF-1 Wolfpack had black around the edge of the canopy and behind it. Today the VF-1 Tomcats *have black paint only in front of the cockpit as an anti-glare device. The VF-2 aircraft used to have the same paint design as VF-1 does today. Now, however, VF-2 has black paint along the sides of the canopy all the way to the tip of the nose.* (Grumman)

The ground instructor pilot can rotate the computer-generated drawings of an actual dogfight to get whatever perspective is necessary.

(Cubic Corporation)

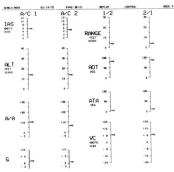

The status of the F-14A and the F-5E are shown here from a printout taken at the beginning of the fight. The date and time (in hours, minutes, seconds, and hundredths of seconds) are shown at the top of the printout. The F-14A is A/C 1.

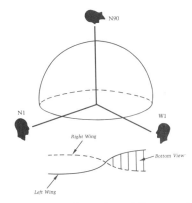

By taking printouts from three different points you can reconstruct the spatial relationships of the two aircraft during the dogfight. N1 is what an observer on the ground looking north would see; W1 is what the same observer would see looking west; and N90 is looking straight down from above the fight.

The ACMR pod that transmits data to the ground antennas is shown in position on a Navy F-4 Phantom.

(Cubic Corporation)

Dogfight with a MiG-21 Simulator

The two pages that follow this one illustrate an actual dogfight between an F-14A and an F-5E. The line illustrations are not drawings or somebody's impression of what the dogfight should have looked like — they are printouts from a teaching device known as the Air Combat Maneuvering Range (ACMR).

The Navy needed a way to take the guesswork out of who got the best shot during practice. There hadn't been any scientific method to know if the gunsight was right on target or if the missile envelope had been reached. Most of the training fights were won or lost at the Officers' Club after hours. The Cubic Corporation with the Navy developed the ACMR to eliminate this guess work and relay exact data to the ground observation station.

The ACMR range where the pilots fly is outside Yuma, Arizona. Antennas are placed throughout the flying area which pick up data from the ACMR pod afixed to the aircraft where a Sparrow missile would ordinarily be carried (see photo above). The data is then relayed by telemetry back to the observation points at Yuma and NAS Miramar.

The system is designed so that the ground instructor pilot can observe the two or more aircraft from any position. By rotating two dials on the console the observer can change the azimuth and elevation; and in so doing look at the aircraft from any height off the ground or from any direction (see illustration above).

The observer can also get a status readout on each aircraft e.g. A/C 1 and the relationship between the two aircraft e.g. 2/1. The information available on each aircraft individually is indicated air speed (IAS), altitude (ALT), angle of attack in units (A/A), and gravitational force (G). The data available between the two aircraft is range, angle off of the tail (AOT) which is how many degrees to the right or left the aircraft is from a line drawn straight back from the other aircraft, antenna train angle (ATA) which is the degrees the antenna is turned from a position straight ahead, and finally the velocity of closure (VC).

The ACMR system captured an F-14A from VF-124 and an F-5E from the Navy Fighter Weapons School and followed the sequence of the fight. The F-5E is used because it is one of the best simulators of the MiG-21 in the free world. Some believe it is better than the MiG-21. In our example A/C 1 is the F-14A and A/C 2 is the F-5E. N90 represents looking down from the top; N1 is looking north from the ground; and W1 is looking west from the ground. The time is listed along the side and from the data you can see that the fight lasts only 57 seconds.

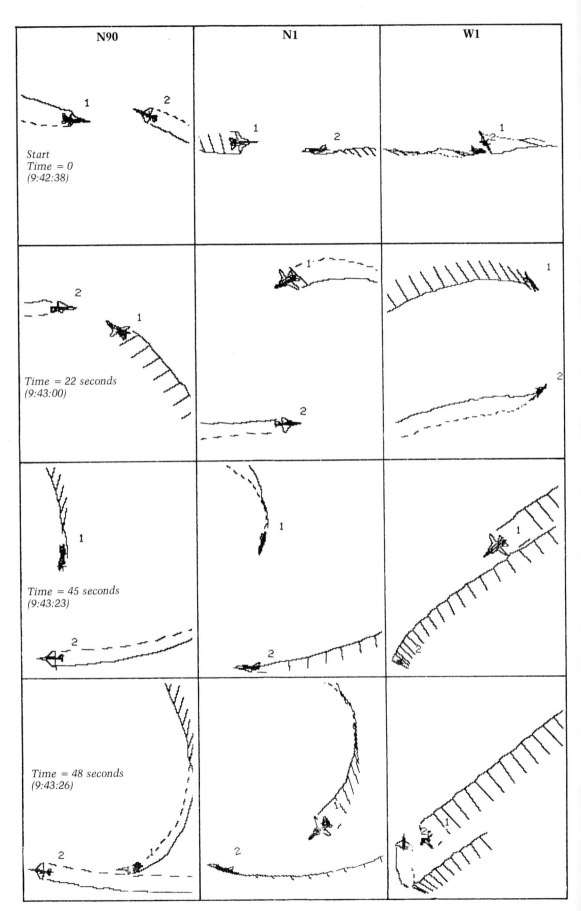

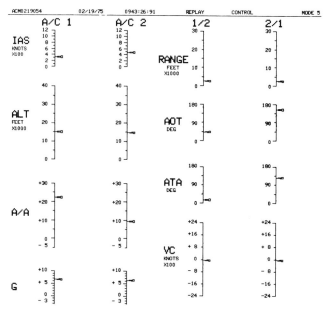

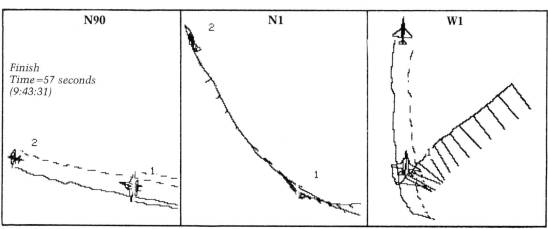

Finish
Time=57 seconds
(9:43:31)

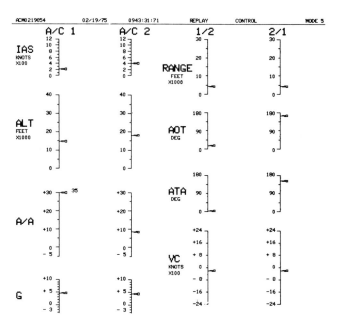

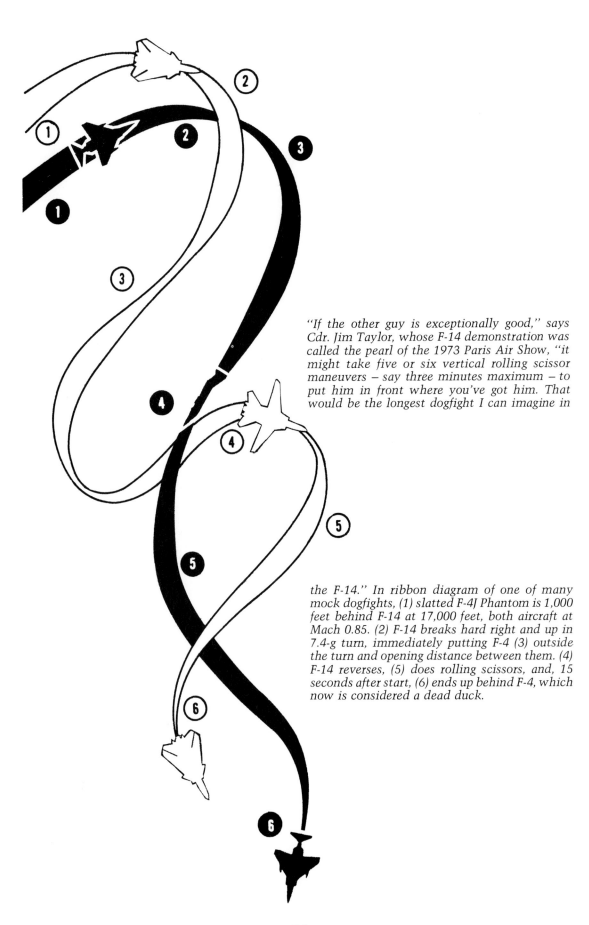

"If the other guy is exceptionally good," says Cdr. Jim Taylor, whose F-14 demonstration was called the pearl of the 1973 Paris Air Show, "it might take five or six vertical rolling scissor maneuvers – say three minutes maximum – to put him in front where you've got him. That would be the longest dogfight I can imagine in the F-14." In ribbon diagram of one of many mock dogfights, (1) slatted F-4J Phantom is 1,000 feet behind F-14 at 17,000 feet, both aircraft at Mach 0.85. (2) F-14 breaks hard right and up in 7.4-g turn, immediately putting F-4 (3) outside the turn and opening distance between them. (4) F-14 reverses, (5) does rolling scissors, and, 15 seconds after start, (6) ends up behind F-4, which now is considered a dead duck.

A series from eight engagements between the F-14 and an F-4 with slotted maneuvering slats. The F-4 was astern four times and the F-14 was astern the other four times. In no case did the F-4 track over 3 seconds from astern. The F-14 pulled 7.3 G's at 35,000 feet at Mach 1.1   (Grumman)

The F-14 Weapons System

The Hughes Airborne Weapons Group Nine (AWG-9) is the heart of F-14. Although the name AWG-9 is the same as the weapon control system in the F-111B, that's where the similarity ends. If you jacked up a car, replaced it with a newer model but left the same license plate on, then that is the similarity between the AWG-9 in the F-111B and the F-14.[35] For one thing, the weight was reduced by 700 pounds, to 1,300. The volume, a total of 28 cubic feet, was reduced 3 cubic feet.[36] The F-111B's AWG-9 could only track 18 targets while the F-14 can track 24. The Navy is continuously finding new applications for the AWG-9 and isn't yet sure of its complete capabilities.

The AWG-9 is made up of a radar, computer, interface between AWG-9 and weapons and the associated displays. The primary purpose of the F-14 is to act as a weapons platform. To that end, then, the primary purpose of the AWG-9 is to control the four weapons it carries — the gun, the *Sidewinder* missile (AIM-9), the *Sparrow* missile (AIM-7) and the *Phoenix* missile (AIM-54).

The AWG-9 weapon control system uses inputs from the radar and in conjunction with the computer, establishes target identities, establishes priorities, processes data for the intercept geometry, establishes launch envelopes and monitors some of the F-14's other black boxes. The size of the AWG-9's computer allows it to perform some additional functions such as navigation solutions.

The AWG-9 Radar

The AWG-9 radar transmits and receives thru a 36 inch diameter planar type flat plated antenna. A quick review of radar techniques will illustrate the power of the AWG-9 system.

The physics of radar is similar to the physics of echoes. Since sound travels at a known speed, and since the time that passes from the shout until its echo return can be measured, the distance to the reflecting surface is known by applying the time-distance formula.

$$\text{rate x time} = \text{distance}$$

With radar, a burst of energy is sent out at a known speed. The system measures the time that passes until it gets back, and like magic, the distance is measured. Radar that works in this fashion is called pulse radar. Pulses are sent out that measure distance. Pulse is the type of radar that became famous in World War II. It was the mainstay during the 1950's and 1960's and is still a very powerful tool today.

Pulse radar works fine as long as air is the backdrop of the target. If the background becomes earth, then the return from the ground clutters the radar scope so badly that the target usually becomes obscured.

A new radar was developed that would see only moving targets. This new radar is called pulse Doppler. Pulse Doppler does not see the background, only targets moving with respect to the ground, so when searching for targets below the horizon, there is no ground clutter. Pulse Doppler gets its name from the Doppler effect.

The Doppler effect is something that everyone has noticed at one time or another. It is particularly noticed when a siren moves toward or away from the listener. If sitting at a park bench an ambulance comes toward a listener and then goes away from him, he would have heard two distinct effects. First, the ambulance's siren would get louder and then quieter. But the frequency would appear to get higher as the ambulance approached, and get lower as it went away. The actual frequency of the siren stays the same. As the siren approaches, the frequency of the siren is getting closer to the frequency already reaching the listener's ear; the opposite is the case as the ambulance leaves. The frequency emitted from the ambulance is getting farther away from those hitting the listener's ear. It's similar to throwing a ball at a wall *moving* toward the listener. The ball comes back faster than if the wall stood still. This phenomenon, called the Doppler effect, is applied to radar.

Pulse Doppler radar tracks the Doppler frequency generated by a moving target as opposed to measuring an echo as does pulse radar. The pulse Doppler is tuned so that anything moving at the speed of the airplane is not picked up. In the F-14, then, the radar in the pulse Doppler mode will only pick up a target and not the ground provided that the

Radar Modes Capabilities

	MODE		PRIME FUNCTION	WEAPONS CAPABILITY	ANTENNA PROGRAM	NOMINAL DETECTION RANGE	TARGET DATA AVAILABLE
PULSE DOPPLER	PD SEARCH (PDS)		LONG RANGE SEARCH AND DETECTION	BORESIGHT MISSILE MODES	+10°, 20°, 40°, OR 65° / 1, 2, 4, OR 8 BAR	115 N.MI.*	RANGE RATE
	RANGE-WHILE-SEARCH (RWS)		LONG RANGE SEARCH, DETECTION & RANGING			90 N.MI.*	RANGE, RANGE RATE, AND ANGLES
	TRACK-WHILE-SCAN (TWS)		SEARCH, DETECTION, AND MULTIPLE TARGET TRACK, AND AIM-54 LAUNCH	AIM-54A (MULTIPLE RELEASE) MAX MISSILE LAUNCH - 52 N.MI.	2 BAR 40° OR 4 BAR 20°	90 N.MI.*	COMPLETE TRACK FILE
	PD SINGLE TARGET TRACK (PDSTT)	VELOCITY TRACK (VT)	LONG RANGE SINGLE TARGET TRACKING AND MISSILE LAUNCH	AIM-54A - 63 N.MI. (MAX) AIM-9G - 1.5 N.MI. TO 10 N.MI. DEPENDING ON ALT/GEOMETRY AIM-7F - 38 N.MI. (MAX)	LOCKON	90 N.MI.*	RANGE, RANGE RATE, AND ANGLES
		JAM ANGLE TRACK (JAT)				DEPENDS ON JAMMING**	ANGLES AND RATES**
	PD RADAR SLAVED (PDRSL)		RADAR ILLUMINATION AND RANGING ON IR TARGET		RADAR IS SLAVED TO IR LINE OF SIGHT	90 N.MI.*	ANGLES, RANGE AND RANGE RATE
PULSE	PULSE SEARCH (PS)		SHORT AND MEDIUM RANGE SEARCH AND DETECTION AND A/G	BORESIGHT MISSILE MODES	+10°m 20°m 40°m IR 65° / 1, 2, 4, OR 8 BAR	62 N.MI.*	CONVENTIONAL PULSE RADAR
	PS SINGLE TARGET TRACK	RANGE TRACK (RT)	SHORT AND MEDIUM RANGE SINGLE-TARGET TRACKING, AND MISSILE LAUNCH	GUN A/G STORES AIM-54A (ACTIVE) - 29 N.MI. AIM-7F(CW) - 29 N.MI. AIM-7E(CW) - 18 N.MI. AIM-9 - 1.5 N.MI. TO 20 N.MI. DEPENDING ON ALT/GEOMETRY	LOCKON	49 N.MI.*	
		JAM ANGLE TRACK (JAT)				DEPENDS ON JAMMING**	ANGLES AND RATES**
	PULSE RADAR SLAVED (PRSL)		RADAR ILLUMINATION AND RANGING ON IR TARGET		SLAVED TO IR/TV SENSOR	49 N.MI.*	ANGLES, RANGE AND RANGE RATE
TRANS-ITIONAL	PILOT RAPID LOCKON (PLM)		PILOT INITIATED RADAR LOCKON	NOT APPLICABLE	2.3° BEAM CENTERED ALONG ADL	5 N.MI.*	RANGE AND ANGLE TRACKING
	VERTICAL SCAN LOCKON (VSL)		RAPID LOCKON TO TARGET IN VERTICAL PLANE		VSL HI +15° TO +55° 2 BAR / VSL LO -15° TO +25° 2 BAR		
	MANUAL RAPID LOCKON (MRL)		RAPID LOCKON TO TARGET LOCATED ANYWHERE IN RADAR FIELD OF VIEW		±10° AZIMUTH 1 BAR IN ELEVATION		

* BASED ON 5 m² TARGET
** ALTITUDE DIFFERENCE RANGING (ADR) CAPABILITY EXISTS

Doppler Target Display

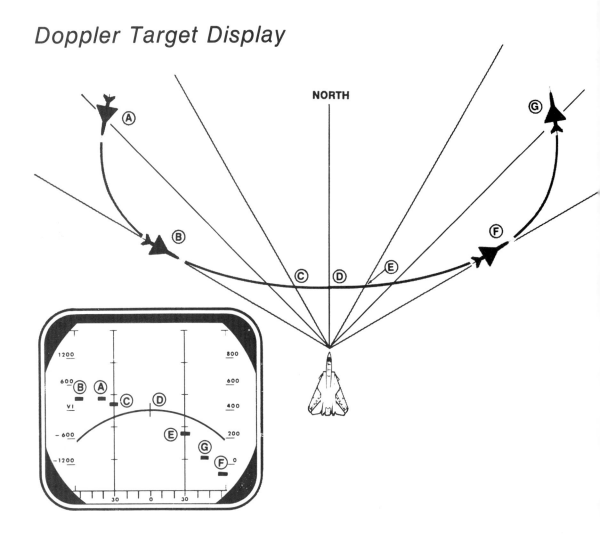

target is coming toward or moving away from the F-14. It stands to reason that a target that is not coming toward, nor moving away, i.e., moving across or abeam, would not exhibit the Doppler effect. The object would not be distinguished from the ground below it. In these cases pulse and not pulse Doppler should be selected.

The Navy's F-4B has a pulse radar only, while the F-4J has a pulse and pulse Doppler radar. There is a big difference, however, between the F-4J and the F-14, even though they both have pulse Doppler. The biggest difference is the F-14's AWG-9 integrated system.

The AWG-9 has six basic modes of radar operation: 4 are in the pulse Doppler mode, 2 in the pulse mode.

Pulse Doppler Modes:	Pulse Doppler Search (PDS)
	Range While Search (RWS)
	Track While Scan (TWS)
	Pulse Doppler Single Target Track (PDSTT)
Pulse Modes:	Pulse Search (PS)
	Pulse Single Target Track (PSTT)

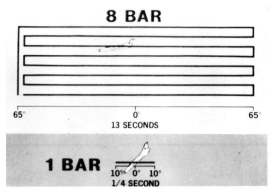

8 BAR

65°   0°   65°
13 SECONDS

1 BAR
10°   0°   10°
1/4 SECOND

The maximum scan pattern of the AWG-9 compared to the minimum pattern. (U.S. Navy/ISD)

The maximum radar antenna search is an 8 bar pattern, 65° to the right and left of the aircraft centerline. The degrees the radar antenna swings to the right or left is azmith and the elevation is broken into bars.

Pulse Doppler Search

This mode is for basic long range detection. PDS gives the maximum range detection — 2 and ½ times that of the F-4J. The information is displayed on the Detailed Data Display (DDD) as raw radar data, in azmith, elevation and range *rate* (rate of closure or separation). Limitation: This mode does not provide target range.

Range While Search

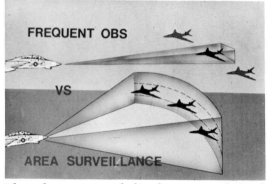

The advantages and disadvantages of Track While Scan (TWS) are shown here. The TWS mode must use a smaller azmith and elevation (bar) combination than Range While Scan (RWS). However, while in RWS important information is unavailable to the NFO which he could get in TWS.   *(U.S. Navy/ISD)*

RWS gives the greatest surveillance volume, combined with range (not to be confused with range rate above). The volume detection area of the AWG-9 in the F-14 is 15 times greater than the F-4J. The RWS mode gives range in addition to *rate*, azmith, and elevation. The information is displayed on the DDD and on the Tactical

Information Display (TID). Limitation: TID does not give heading, speed, or altitude of targets. There is a slight decay in range detection.

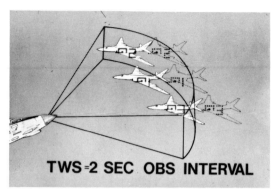

TWS-2 SEC OBS INTERVAL

The Track While Scan mode uses the computer to track targets so that the hostile aircraft won't receive an electronic indication that they are being tracked. The computer must be updated every two seconds, so the scan pattern must be one that returns every two seconds: plus or minus 40°, 2 bar, or plus or minus 20°, 4 bar. (U.S. Navy/ISD)

Track While Scan

This is the exotic mode that tracks 24 targets simultaneously. The radar sweeps across every two seconds, stores the targets' last known position in the computer, and estimates where each of targets will appear next. The computer may now compute heading, altitude, speed, launch zones, firing priorities, and other tactical information. Limitation: The TWS mode is for the launch of the *Phoenix* missile only. Since the radar must see the targets every two seconds for the computer to correlate, the azmith and bar (elevation) combination must be one that repeats each two seconds, i.e. ± 40°, 2 bar or ± 20°, 4 bar.

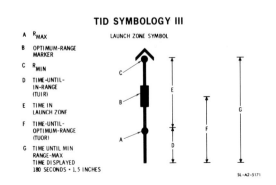

TID SYMBOLOGY III

A   R$_{MAX}$
B   OPTIMUM-RANGE MARKER
C   R$_{MIN}$
D   TIME-UNTIL-IN-RANGE (TUIR)
E   TIME IN LAUNCH ZONE
F   TIME-UNTIL-OPTIMUM-RANGE (TUOR)
G   TIME UNTIL MIN RANGE-MAX TIME DISPLAYED 180 SECONDS · 1.5 INCHES

LAUNCH ZONE SYMBOL

SL-A2-5171

The velocity vector gives the NFO much information as he observes various aircraft on the Tactical Information Display. (U.S. Navy/ISD)

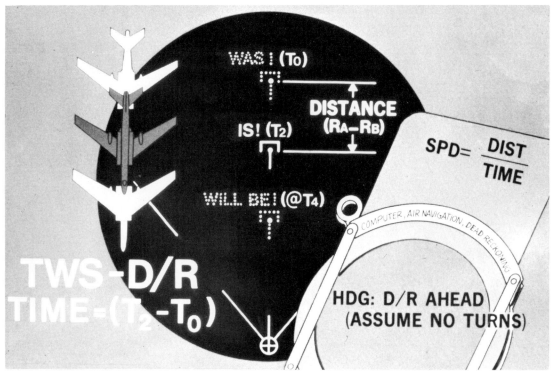

The AWG-9 computer performs dead reckoning using the fundamentals of a pilot's navigational computer. *(U.S. Navy/ISD)*

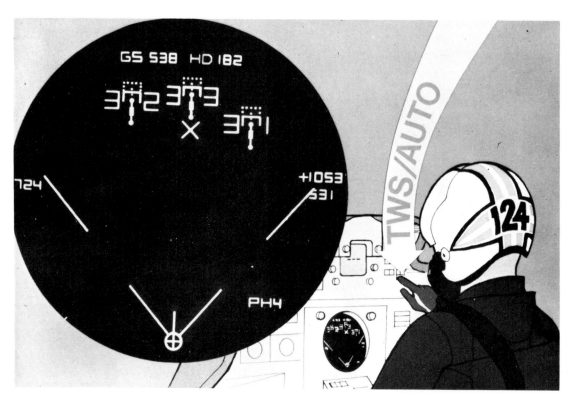

The NFO sees targets move across the Tactical Information Display (TID) toward his aircraft in this fashion. Ground speed and heading of selected targets are displayed at the top of the TID. The TWS/Auto mode lets the computer select the greatest concentration of targets and center the coverage. *(U.S. Navy/ISD)*

Pulse Doppler Single Target Track

This mode provides maximum range for a *Phoenix* missile attack. It also gives the maximum range in track. PDSTT is similar to the capability of the F-4J's AWG-10 system, except for the increase in range. The F-4 radar can see many targets, just as the AWG-9 radar can. If the NFO wants to fire at one of the targets, he must first track it, by locking on with the radar. Once this happens, all other targets on the F-4 radar (or the F-14 radar in any track mode other than TWS) disappear. The second disadvantage of the F-4 radar is that once you lock on, the target aircraft, if he has ECM equipment, will know he is being tracked by radar. The beauty of Track While Scan over the F-4 radar or other modes of the F-14 radar system is the computer. The computer does the tracking while the radar antenna continues to scan the area. This makes the target aircraft believe that he isn't being tracked — that some hostile aircraft is simply scanning the area. Limitation: The PDSTT has poor tracking capabilities when the target isn't coming or moving away, since this is pulse Doppler.

Pulse Search

Pulse radar is used for air-to-air search or ground mapping. In pulse, there is no range *rate*, only range versus azmith. The full spectrum of radar antenna pattern combinations — 10°, 20°, 40° or 65° in azmith and 1, 2, 4, or 8 bars elevation — is available. There is no abeam limitation in pulse radar as there is in Doppler. In Pulse Doppler, an F-14 rendezvous on an orbiting tanker would be difficult. The target would be strong only while the tanker was closing on the F-14. While it was abeam, the target would be lost; while departing it would be weak. In this situation, good old pulse radar would do a better job. Limitation: The range in pulse isn't as great as in pulse Doppler, and search below the horizon is difficult.

Pulse Single Target Track

The major advantage of pulse radar is that there is no loss of target in the beam aspect. It follows that in tracking, if an F-14 were following a target, which was to turn at right angles to the F-14's path of flight, pulse Doppler would be a degraded mode. Pulse radar would continue to track the target regardless of its direction of flight.[37]

Air Combat Maneuvering Radar Modes

There are additional refinements to the radar system designed especially for use during ACM. These modes allow the pilot or NFO to automatically acquire the target aircraft during high G maneuvers. The radar actually turns the corner for the pilot, so that he can fire without having to line up the nose of the aircraft on the target. These modes also let the pilot keep his head out of the cockpit during the dogfight.

Pilot Lockon Mode (PLM)

This mode allows the pilot to lockon to a target directly out in front of the airplane.

Vertical Scan Lockon (VSL)

This is an ideal mode for acquiring a lockon while pulling into a maneuvering target. The radar sweeps up and down in front of the F-14, in a narrow beam. Whatever crosses the beam within the vertical limits of the radar antenna scan will be locked up.

NFO Rapid Lockon (NRL)

This is a manual mode that the NFO uses. He points the radar antenna in the direction of the target. It's similar to shooting from the hip; NFO's and pilots find it the least valuable of the three ACM modes.

Other Features

Built-In Test

The extra storage in the AWG-9 computer makes it possible to have a built-in test capability. The NFO can go through a series of checks before a flight, during a flight, and after a flight. These tests can isolate a problem within the various systems in the aircraft. The NFO can perform an inflight test by selecting that mode on the AWG-9 computer address panel. Once the problem has been isolated, the NFO can call the squadron maintenance department. Many times the maintenance personnel can correct the problem over the air, thus avoiding the expense of having the F-14 return to base.

Infrared (IR) Search

The infrared mode provides detection in the airspace that can be used in conjunction with the radar. It is most effective against high altitude after-burning targets. The IR sensor can be slaved to the radar, or it can search independently. F-14's have picked up SR-71's at high altitudes over long distances.

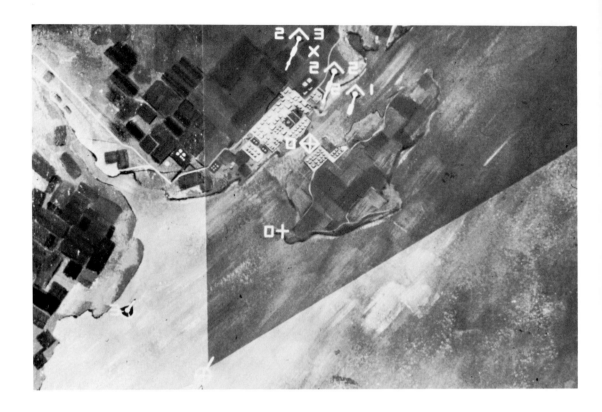

The Tactical Information Display (TID) represents the real world as the radar sees it. The information on the TID is all the NFO needs to know to make a proper evaluation. The numbers on either side of the targets represent priority of firing and altitude. The diamond with a cross represents a surface target; the target outside the view of the radar's field of view is Data Link generated, and a friendly target. Data Link can send up to the F-14 eight additional targets that can add to the NFO's perception of the situation. (U.S. Navy/ISD)

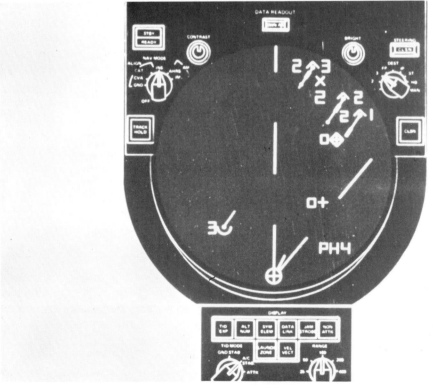

Electro-optical (EO)

The F-14 does not currently have electro-optical capabilities. However, the IR sensor under the nose of the F-14 can be replaced with an EO sensor.

By selecting the Vertical Scan Lockon switch of the Air Combat Maneuvering mode of the AWG-9 radar, the pilot need only roll into the target to acquire a radar lockon. *(U.S. Navy/ISD)*

ACM MODES

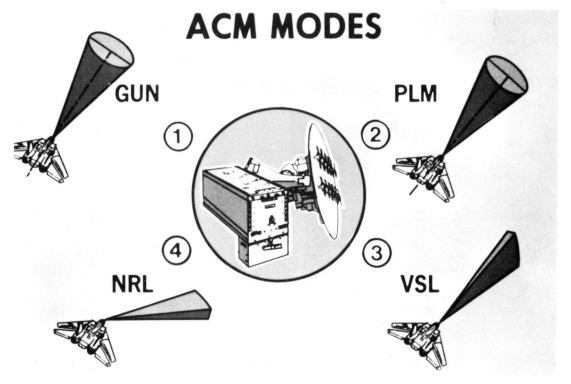

VSL Beam Coverage

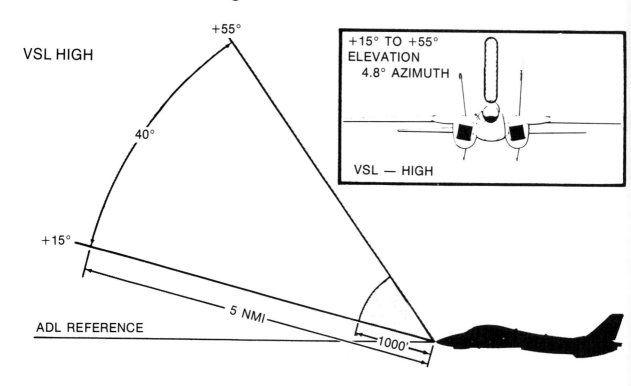

VSL HIGH

+55°

40°

+15°

+15° TO +55°
ELEVATION
4.8° AZIMUTH

VSL — HIGH

5 NMI

ADL REFERENCE

1000'

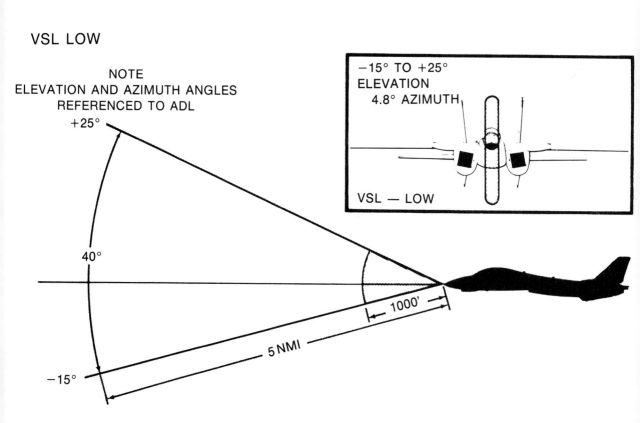

VSL LOW

NOTE
ELEVATION AND AZIMUTH ANGLES
REFERENCED TO ADL

+25°

−15° TO +25°
ELEVATION
4.8° AZIMUTH

VSL — LOW

40°

1000'

5 NMI

−15°

F-14 Weapons

To fulfill its multi-mission role, the F-14 carries four major weapons, plus air-to-ground ordnance. The particular mission determines the missile mix. In the Fleet Air Defense role, the F-14 would carry all *Phoenix*, with a small complement of Sidewinders and the necessary rounds for the internally mounted M61 cannon. In an air superiority role, the F-14 would carry *Sparrows* and *Sidewinders.* These options are part of the multi-role concept of the F-14.

The AIM-54 Phoenix Missile

The *Phoenix* Missile is designed to handle the threat of long range air-to-air, surface-to-surface, or air-to-surface missiles, and of course threat aircraft. The *Phoenix* is a semi-active radar homing missile, with a terminal active radar phase. The *Phoenix* works in the pulse Doppler mode.

The Sparrow III AIM 7E/F

The AIM-7 *Sparrow* missile is a semi-active radar-homing air-to-air missile. Although both the AIM-7E and the AIM-7F look alike, there is a difference. The AIM-7E is guided by continuous wave only, while the AIM-7F is guided on continuous wave or

Three versions of the Sidewinder *missile. Top to bottom: AIM-9B, AIM-9D, and AIM-9C.*
(U.S. Navy)

The Sidewinder AIM9G/H

The *Sidewinder* is the infamous heat-seeking missile that was used heavily by the Navy pilot in Vietnam. The *Sidewinders* of the past have required the pilot to line up the aircraft with the target until it was time to fire. The current *Sidewinders* have SEAM, which stands for *Sidewinder* Expanded Acquisition Mode. These SEAM *Sidewinders* start tracking the target before they come off the aircraft rail. This is accomplished by slaving the seeker head slaved to the radar. The *Sidewinder* is a short range missile only.

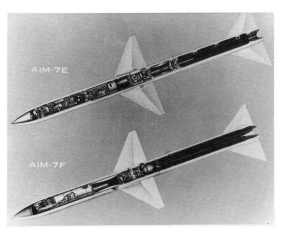

Interior views of the AIM-7E and AIM-7F Sparrow *missiles. The AIM-7F is guided by either pulse Doppler or continuous wave (CW) illumination. The AIM-7E is guided by CW only.*
(U.S. Navy)

pulse Doppler. The AIM-7F has an improved motor which will allow it to go after higher altitude targets. The F version has closer minimum range, which makes it more valuable in an ACM environment.

The F-14A's M61 20mm cannon carries 675 rounds of ammunition and is capable of firing 6,000 rounds a minute. (Grumman)

The M61 Vulcan Cannon

The M61 is a 20mm internally mounted six-barrel cannon, with a firing speed of 6,000 rounds per minute. The F-14 carries 676 rounds of ammunition. The gunsight solution is provided by the AWG-9 digital computer utilizing inertial and radar inputs, or it can be fired in boresight.

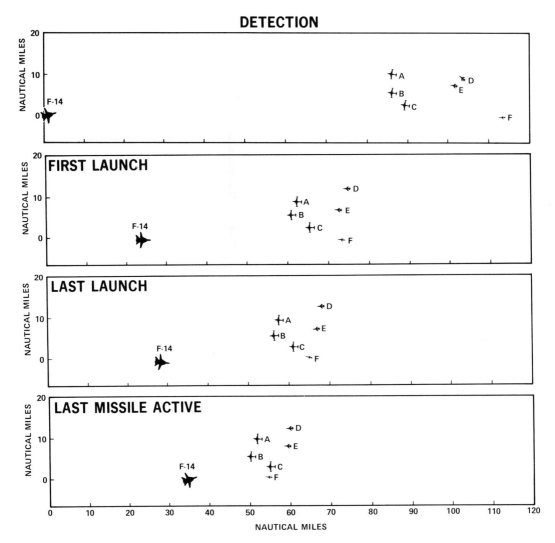

DETECTION

FIRST LAUNCH

LAST LAUNCH

LAST MISSILE ACTIVE

NAUTICAL MILES

Phoenix Capability

On November 21, 1973, CDR John R. (Smoke) Wilson made aviation warfare history when he piloted along with LCDR Jack H. Hawver, USN, his NFO, the first aircraft to simultaneously guide six *Phoenix* missiles at six separate targets. The initial detection of all six targets was between 85 and 115 nautical miles. The first missile was fired when the drones were between 30 and 50 nautical miles away. The F-14A was at Mach 0.8 at 28,000 feet. The time between first missile firing and last missile firing was 37 seconds. The aircrew chose the first three targets, the AWG-9 computer chose the second three. One drone was nonfunctional and one missile had an internal failure. The other four missiles were direct hits. During the course of this test, all six missiles were satisfactorily guiding simultaneously on the six different targets. The *Phoenix* missile, as

of December, 1974, demonstrated a success rate of about 90 per cent.

The *Phoenix* has also demonstrated the capability to attack high and very low targets. A BQM-34E simulating a backfire bomber at 48,000 feet traveling at 1.5 Mach was 110 nautical miles away when an F-14A traveling at Mach 1.5 and 44,000 feet in the track-while-scan mode launched a *Phoenix* and made a lethal hit. An F-14A at Mach .72 and 10,000 feet launched a *Phoenix* at a BQM-34A traveling at .75 Mach only 50 feet off the water 22 miles away. It, too, was a lethal hit.

This high altitude, low altitude multi-target capability is what gives the F-14 its impressive credentials. This capability makes the F-14 difficult to compare with other aircraft in terms of one F-14 being worth 2 or 3 or even 4 F-4s because of the difference in capability — the F-14 can simply do things the others can't.

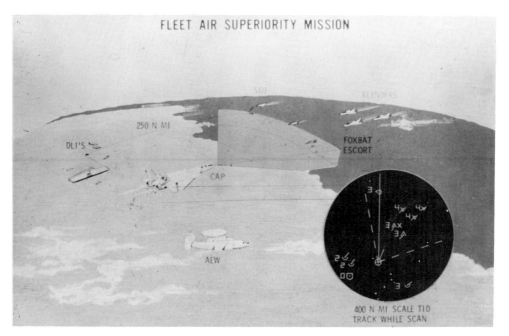

A typical Fleet Air Defense (Superiority) mission would look like this. The F-14's radar can scan up to 400 miles. (U.S. Navy/ISD)

The Mission

The Mission of the United States Navy is to provide strategic deterrence, sea control, naval presence, and projection of power.[38] The best way to support these missions is to provide aircraft carriers. There is one alternative — to pave the world — but short of that, the aircraft carrier appears to be the answer.[39] Whenever we have built airfields in foreign countries we have always run the risk of having them taken over by the nationalistic zeal that might be currently in vogue. In fact, during the Yom Kippur War in 1973, our European allies would not let American aircraft use their airbases for fear that their oil supplies would be cut off by the Arabs. The need for aircraft carriers becomes even greater under these circumstances and so does their protection. The F-14 gives the aircraft carrier a quantum leap in protection with the multiple shot *Phoenix* capability. The range of the F-14 compared to the F-4 gives the carrier added capability to its command and control both in terms of radar surveillance volume and ultimate range of the F-14 itself to handle Fleet Air Defense away from the fleet.

Looking back at the requirements for the F6D *Missileer* to combat the stand-off missile capability — both air-to-surface and surface-to-surface — the need never went away, but in fact, became greater. Added to that aggravation was the reduced number of aircraft carriers funded, which caused a reduction in carrier deck real estate available. To keep F-4 *Phantoms* on carriers when and if the number of carriers is reduced would reduce the overall effectiveness of the Navy to fulfill its mission. The F-14 helps make up for the reduction of numbers with its increased capability.

The mission of the F-14, like the F-4, is to provide Fleet Air Defense, Air Superiority, and interdiction. In the Fleet Air Defense role the F-14 — with its *Phoenix* missiles — clearly shows its added capability. The AWG-9 weapon system alone would give the F-14 added capability in detection. The air superiority capabilities of the F-14 are second to none. Historically, dogfights that start at high altitudes and at fast supersonic speeds end up at lower altitudes and at speeds between .7 Mach and 1.2 Mach. The F-14 with its variable sweep wing retains a large advantage at the slower speeds and lower altitudes over any known threat. The interdiction or bombing role of the F-14 is not that well documented at this time. The capabilities are built into the computer system and airframe. To date, however, the Navy has concentrated on the two primary missions of the aircraft.

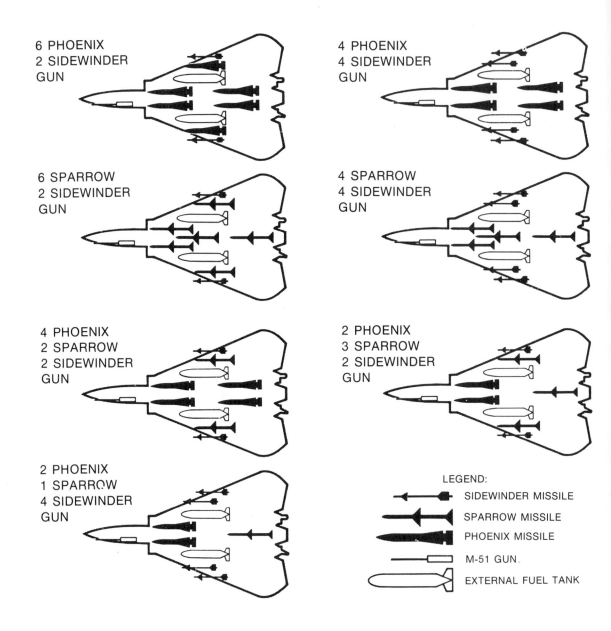

6 PHOENIX
2 SIDEWINDER
GUN

4 PHOENIX
4 SIDEWINDER
GUN

6 SPARROW
2 SIDEWINDER
GUN

4 SPARROW
4 SIDEWINDER
GUN

4 PHOENIX
2 SPARROW
2 SIDEWINDER
GUN

2 PHOENIX
3 SPARROW
2 SIDEWINDER
GUN

2 PHOENIX
1 SPARROW
4 SIDEWINDER
GUN

LEGEND:

SIDEWINDER MISSILE

SPARROW MISSILE

PHOENIX MISSILE

M-51 GUN

EXTERNAL FUEL TANK

Some of the many combinations of weapons the F-14 can carry. *(U.S. Navy)*

The F-14 provides Fleet Air Defense as the F-4 typically did in Vietnam with two methods. The first is BARCAP. BARCAP stands for Barrier Combat Air Patrol. The BARCAP missions call for the F-14 to patrol at long distances from the fleet for the fleet's defense, but also to position themselves between the threat and the carrier strike force. The second role is called FORCECAP. FORCECAP (FORCAP) is similar to BARCAP but is usually closer to the carrier and under positive control of the carrier.

In the air superiority role the F-14 fulfills the MIGCAP and TARCAP roles. TARCAP (Target Combat Air Patrol) calls for the F-14 to protect the strike force going in, during, and coming out of the target area. This is sometimes called fighter escort. MIGCAP is just what it looks like — looking for MiGs. The only purpose an F-14 would have in this role is hunting for any airborne MiGs and destroying them.*

The F-14 can handle all of these typical F-4 roles. The increased radar volume and distance allows the F-14 to give increased

*I speak here of airborne only because of the ROE (Rules of Engagement) that prevailed in the U.S.'s most recent war which precluded attacking aircraft on the ground.

information to the fleet during the F-14's fleet air defense role; the maneuvering capability, large selection of weapons, and AWG-9 weapons system lets the F-14 take care of any air threat.

The F-14 represents a long wait for the U.S. Navy to have an aircraft capable of fulfilling the Navy missions. The *Tomcat* has designed into it the growth potential to become a complete family of airplanes. A reconnaissance pod is already developed which will allow the F-14 to become an RF-14. The potential for the F-14B and F-14C was designed into the *Tomcat* from the beginning. The Navy would idealistically like to have all of its missions performed by one type airframe. This is not realistic, but the F-14 was designed to have the potential to assume many roles. In that sense, then, the F-14 differs from the F6D *Missileer*, which was cancelled because it was able to perform only one role.

With the *Tomcat's* ability to fulfill the Fleet Air Defense requirement, the Air Superiority role, and the interdiction strikes, the F-14 should be around for a long time. With its potential for taking over the role of other carrier aircraft, it may be streaking the skies even longer.

The USS Enterprise *underway during the F-14's first deployment.* (U.S. Navy)

Portrait of VF-1 during their first deployment. (U.S. Navy)

Notes

1. Declassified material, Douglas Aircraft Company, n.p., p. 11.
2. Ibid., p. 16.
3. Richard Austin Smith, "The $7-Billion Contract That Changed the Rules," *Fortune,* n.p. Mach 1963, p. 101.
4. Navy Fighter Weapons School, "Topgun Dictums".
5. Lloyd Edward Allen, "The New Soviet Navy: An International Political and Foreign Policy Analysis," unpublished A.M. thesis, The University of Texas at Austin, December 1972.
6. "The Growing Threat: Soviets Push Advances in Fighters," *Aviation Week and Space Technology,* October 18, 1971.
7. Ibid.
8. Smith, p. 97.
9. Kurt H. Miska, *General Dynamics F-111A to F & FB-111A,* London: Profile Publications Limited, 1973, p. 2.
10. Personal interview with Howard Ruggles, Hughes Aircraft, Canoga Park, California, May 28, 1974.
11. Personal interview with Dr. W.R. Laidlaw, President, Flight Systems, (formerly special assistant to Dr. John Foster, Director of Defense Research and Engineering [DDR&E]), Newport Beach, California, June, 1974.
12. Laidlaw.
13. Laidlaw.
14. J. Richard Elliott, Jr., "Wing and a Prayer," *Barrons,* August 30, 1965, p. 15.
15. Laidlaw.
16. Laidlaw.
17. Michael Pelehach, Vice President Grumman Aerospace Corporation and F-14 Program Manager, lecture and subsequent paper for National Aerospace Engineering and Manufacturing Meeting, San Diego, October 1-3, 1974, "F-14A Status Report: Operational Capabilities, Program Accomplishments, and Cost," Society of Automotive Engineers, 400 Commonwealth Drive, Warrendale, PA 15096.
18. Michael Pelehach, F-14 Program Director, Joseph Rees, F-14 Deputy Program Director, Robert W. Kress, F-14 Engineering Manager, "Case History of Modern Fighter Design: Dogfighter-Plus," *Grumman Horizons,* 1970, 9:1, p. 12.
19. Personal interview with Capt. L.S. (Scotty) Lamoreaux, USN, former F-14 Project Coordinator, COMFIT/ AEWWINGPAC, NAS Miramar, CA March, 1974.
20. Dave Polis, Military Writer, *San Diego Union,* March 22, 1974.
21. *Preliminary Natops Flight Manual,* NAVAIR 01-F14AAA-1, Naval Air Systems Command, 1 November 1973, p. 104.
22. Ibid., p. 100.
23. Capt. L.S. Lamoreaux, USN from a briefing given to the Aviation and Space Writers Association at NAS Miramar, April 17, 1974.
24. "Topgun Dictums."
25. "Topgun Dictums."
26. Laidlaw, Sept. 1974.
27. H. H. Hurt, Jr., *Aerodynamics for Naval Aviators,* NAVAIR 00-80T-80, Revised 1965, p. 23.
28. CDR. John R. (Smoke) Wilson, Jr., USN, unpublished briefing paper COMNAVAIRPAC, NAS North Island, CA May, 1974.
29. Personal interview with Mike Ciminera, Grumman Aerospace Corporation, Bethpage, New York, November 12, 1974.
30. *Tomcat News,* "See Possible 40% Increase in F-14 Envelope," Summer 1974, p. 7.
31. Robert W. Kress, Deputy Director of Project & Technology Development (formerly F-14 Engineering Manager), Arnold B. Whitaker, Technical Adviser, Systems Technology, "Is the Swingwing Unbeatable?" *Grumman Aerospace Horizons,* Vol. 10, No. 1, pp. 12-13.
32. Ibid., p. 13.
33. Clark Martin, "F-14 Shows Dogfight Capabilities," *Aviation Week & Space Technology,* June 4, 1973.
34. Tomcat News, p. 7.

35. Personal interview with Howard Ruggles, Hughes Aircraft Company, at NAS Miramar, California, April 17, 1974.

36. Barry Miller, "AWG-9 Provides Multi-Target Capability," *Aviation Week & Space Technology*, March 19, 1973.

37. Personal conversation with Sam Ammons, Grumman Aerospace Corporation, San Diego, California, January 1, 1975.

38. VADM Stanfield Turner, USN, "Missions of the U.S. Navy," *Naval War College Review*, March-April 1974, pp. 2-17.

39. Personal interview with RADM Obie Oberg, USN, USS *Enterprise*, at sea 200 miles southwest of San Diego, June 1974.

40. David A. Brown, "Accelerated Testing Set for F-14A," *Aviation Week & Space Technology*, December 20, 1971.

The first paint scheme on the first VF-1 F-14 was changed with the later version to a wider stripe and the omission of the words "Wolf Pack." (U.S. Navy)

Appendix A

Traditionally, aerospace corporations make 20 pre-production aircraft for testing. These aircraft are used to get the bugs out of the ultimate production aircraft. The listing below explains what each pre-production aircraft was used for in the testing program. Pre-production aircraft are easy to spot because of the larger than production overwing fairings or upper-surface fences on the first 12 aircraft.

No. 1 Envelope exploration and high speed aircraft. Crashed on second flight. (For dates, see Appendix of significant dates in the history of the F-14).

No. 6 Sent to Pt. Mugu for missile separation work. (Lost during missile separation.)

No. 7 Used as the F-14B prototype to test the Pratt & Whitney F401-PW-400 engine.

No. 8 This aircraft was used to develop aerodynamic performance data.

No. 9 Sent to Pt. Mugu for AWG-9 analysis by Hughes Aircraft Co.

No. 10 Dedicated for carrier suitability. No. 10 aircraft crashed on June 30, 1972 at The Naval Air Test Center, Patuxent River, Maryland.

A VF-2 Tomcat *pulls 6.5 Gs during an Indian Ocean Airshow 150 feet off the deck. Condensation from high G maneuvers is often seen but seldom photographed.* (U.S. Navy)

No. 1X The No. 1 aircraft was replaced with the No. 12 aircraft and redesignated 1X, with the same assignment.

No. 2 Had the major role in the exploration of high angle of attack regime.

The F-14A has flown through plus 90° to minus 90° in all configurations.

No. 3. This aircraft was dedicated to structural limit investigation.

No. 4 Used in avionics testing at the Pt. Mugu facility in California. The AWG-9 and the Phoenix missile were evaluated.

No. 5 Sent to Pt. Mugu for systems and feasibility analysis.

No. 11 Sent to Pt. Mugu for Grumman to test systems other than the weapons system.

No. 12 This aircraft replaced aircraft No. One.

No. 13 Used for radiation and electomagnetic analysis in Grumman's anechoic chamber.

No. 14 Used for maintenance studies.

No. 15 Assigned to pilot training.

No. 16 Assigned to pilot training.

No. 17 Replaced No. 10.

No. 18 Assigned to pilot training.

No. 19 Assigned to pilot training.

No. 20 Sent to Pt. Mugu for weather testing.[40]

APPENDIX B

Significant milestones in the History of the F-14

	FROM:	TO:
• Preliminary Studies and Pre-concept Formulation Work	January 1966	September 1967
• Concept Formulation — VFX	September 1967	1 January 1968
• Contract Definition	January 1968	July 1968
• Development Contract Paper (DCP) No. 60 approved by SEC DEF authorizing release of VFX RFP	On 18 June 1968	
• RFP released to industry. Five contractors submitted proposals for Contract Definition Phase (CDP)	On 21 June 1968	
• CDP contracts awarded to five contractors	On 17 July 1968	
• Formal Contract Definition	17 July 1968	1 October 1968
• Source Selection Plan established	On 25 September 1968	
• Proposals received from contractors for engineering development and production	On 1 October 1968	
• Sustaining Effort	1 October 1968	3 February 1968
• Evaluation of proposals completed	On 13 December 1968	
• Presentations to SSA made by SSAC and SSEB. SSA concurred with recommendation to retain Grumman and McDonnell in the competition	On 15 December 1968	
• CNO and SECNAV briefed on results of SSEB, SSAC and SSA evaluations and recommendations		
• DDR&E briefed on the F-14 Source Selection	On 17 December 1968	
• DOD officially released information announcing elimination of remaining three contractors from competition	On 17 December 1968	
• Final revisions to their proposals submitted by Grumman and McDonnell	On 5 January 1969	
• Announcement of Award to Grumman	On 14 January 1969	
• RDT&E Contract Signed	On 3 February 1969	
• Design Configuration Freeze	March 1969	
• ILSMPC completed	On 21 March 1969	
• First drawing release	On 8 May 1969	
• Contractual Mock-up Review completed	On 23 May 1969	
• Started Detail Parts Fabrication	June 1969	
• Management Systems Demonstration	18 August 1969	25 Sept 1969
• NASA Validation of A/C Perf. Characteristics	On 16 September 1969	
• ILS Training Conference completed	On 20 September 1969	
• Started EMMA Assembly	November 1969	
• Wing Pivot Bearing Test Article completed	November 1969	
• SITS arrived at Pt. Mugu	On 21 January 1970	

- AN/AWG-9 Computer and Development Test Equipment (DTE) delivered and installed in SITS at Pt. Mugu — On 2 February 1970
- F-14B Proposal Submitted — On 27 February 1970
- ATE (Advanced Technology Engine) for "B" version awarded to Pratt & Whitney (Fla.) — On 27 February 1970
- Boron Stabilizer Fabrication Completed — On 20 March 1970
- Started Wing Pivot Development Test #9 (at LTV) — On 15 April 1970
- Completed Boron Stabilizer Static Test Series — On 8 May 1970
- XTF30-P-412 Ground Test Engine received Inlet compatibility static testing started — On 18 May 1970
- Wing Pivot Development Test #9 suspended by fatigue failure of two lower lugs at 1.2 times life — On 2 June 1970
- Engine/Inlet tests satisfactory completed — On 9 July 1970
- Final NAVAIR Mockup (EMMA) Demonstration Completed — On 23 July 1970
- Satisfactorily completed 12,000 equivalent flight hours — 2 X life — on the Boron Stabilizer Fatigue Test — On 1 September 1970
- Preliminary fit check of F-14B (F-401) mockup engine in EMMA nacelle accomplished — On 15 September 1970
- F-14B Bilateral Document Signed — On 30 September 1970
- Aircraft #1 completed six hours of engine runs and taxi trials — On 14 December 1970
- F-14A Aircraft #1 First Flight — On 21 December 1970
- F-14A Aircraft #1 crashed during a landing approach in its second flight — On 30 December 1970
- First VAST Station System Acceptance Test completed — On 29 January 1971
- Wing Pivot Test No. 9A passed 7000 test hours (15,120 equivalent flight hours) — On 1 February 1971
- The TF 30-P-412 Engine (P&W) for the F-14A completed the Model Qualification Test with higher than spec thrust ratings — On 5 March 1971
- F-14B F401-PW-400 Engine Installation and Removal Demonstration — On 28 April 1971
- Aircraft #2 completed taxi runs — On 22 May 1971
- Aircraft #2 First Flight — On 24 May 1971
- Aircraft #1X First Flight — On 31 August 1971
- Aircraft #1X Supersonic Flight — On 16 September 1971
- Aircraft #4 First Flight — On 7 October 1971
- First weapon systems aircraft (A/C #4) arrived at Pt. Mugu, California — On 30 October 1971
- Aircraft #5 First Flight — On 26 November 1971
- NPE I started — On 2 December 1971
- Aircraft #6 First Flight — On 10 December 1971
- Aircraft #5 arrived at Pt. Mugu, Calif. — On 12 December 1971

- Successfully completed 2X life (12,000 equivalent flight hours) fatigue test on wing carry through box beam (TB-1X)   On 12 December 1971
- NPE I successfully completed   On 16 December 1971
- Aircraft #3 First Flight   On 28 December 1971
- Aircraft #9 First Flight   On 28 December 1971
- Aircraft #8 First Flight   On 31 December 1971
- Aircraft #9 arrived at Pt. Mugu, California   On 10 January 1972
- Aircraft #6 arrived at Pt. Mugu, California   On 15 January 1972
- Aircraft #4 bailed to Hughes Aircraft Corporation   On 25 January 1972
- External/Internal Lighting Review at Pt. Mugu completed   On 1-2 February 1972
- Aircraft #10 First Flight   On 29 February 1972
- Aircraft #11 First Flight   On 6 March 1972
- Aircraft #11 arrived at Pt. Mugu, California   On 24 March 1972
- Aircraft #10 ferried to Patuxent   On 6 April 1972
- Aircraft #9 bailed to Hughes Aircraft Corporation   On 11 April 1972
- Aircraft #13 First Flight   On 2 May 1972
- Aircraft #14 First Flight   On 6 June 1972
- Aircraft #00 makes first catapult launch from USS Forestal   On 15 June 1972
- Aircraft #00 makes first Carrier landing on USS Forestal   On 28 June 1972
- MMEI (Modified Maintenance Engineering Inspection) Completed   On 29 June 1972
- Aircraft #10 crashed   On 30 June 1972
- NPE (West) started   On 6 July 1972
- NPE II (East) started   On 10 July 1972
- NPE II (West) completed   On 23 July 1972
- Aircraft #15 First Flight   On 01 August 1972
- Aircraft #13 to Anechoic Chamber   On 02 August 1972
- NPE II (HAC) Completed   On 10 August 1972
- Aircraft #16 First Flight   On 11 August 1972
- NPE II (East) Completed   On 15 August 1972
- Aircraft #18 First Flight   On 12 September 1972
- Aircraft #16 Accepted   On 27 September 1972
- VX-4 OPEVAL Started   On 28 September 1972
- Aircraft #16 delivered to Pt. Mugu   On 01 October 1972
- Aircraft #18 delivered to NAS Miramar   On 08 October 1972
- Aircraft #19 First Flight   On 13 October 1972
- VF-1 and VF-2 commissioned at NAS Miramar   On 14 October 1972
- Aircraft #15 delivered to Pt. Mugu   On 23 October 1972
- Aircraft #17 First Flight   On 24 October 1972
- Aircraft #17 delivered to Patuxent   On 30 October 1972
- Aircraft #20 First Flight   On 21 November 1972
- Received No. 1 F401 (XD18) Ground Test Engine (F-14B)   On 22 November 1972
- Aircraft #21 First Flight   On 27 November 1972
- Crew Escape System Complete   On 6 February 1973
- Weapons Loading Demo at Pt. Mugu Completed   On 9 February 1973

APPENDIX C

F-14A FIRST FLIGHTS AND DELIVERY (DD-250) DATES

A/C No.	Delivered to Date	Buro No.	First Flight	DD-250	R&D Mission or Production	Location
1	1	157980	12/21/70	—	—	—
2	2	157981	5/24/71	5/27/71	Low Speed	CTO
1X	3	157991	8/31/71	9/2/71	High Speed	CTO
4	4	157983	10/7/71	10/26/71	Navy	HAC
5	5	157984	11/26/71	12/3/71	AWCS Sys. Demo	GAC
6	6	157985	12/10/71	12/18/71	—	—
3	7	157982	12/28/71	1/4/72	Structural	CTO
9	8	157988	12/28/71	12/29/71	HAC AWS	NMC
8	9	157987	12/31/71	1/14/72	Navy	PAX
10	10	157989	2/29/72	2/29/72	—	—
11	11	157990	3/6/72	3/17/72	AWCS Sys. Demo	GAC
13	12	158612	5/2/72	5/12/72	Funct. Compatibility	GAC
14	13	158613	6/6/72	6/9/72	Rel./Maint. Demo	PAX
15	14	158614	8/1/72	8/31/72	Production	PAX
16	15	158615	8/11/72	9/27/72	Production	NMC (VX4)
18	16	158617	9/12/72	10/6/72	Production	NMC (VX4)
19	17	158618	10/31/72	10/31/72	Production	NMC (VX4)
17	18	158616	10/23/72	11/14/72	CVA	PAX
20	19	158619	11/21/72	12/15/72	Production	PAX
21	20	158620	11/27/72	12/31/72	Production	Miramar (VF124)
22	21	158621	12/11/72	1/19/73	Production	Norfolk (PAR)
23	22	158622	2/3/73	3/24/73	Production	Miramar (VF124)
24	23	158623	2/20/73	4/14/73	Production	Miramar (VF124)
25	24	158624	3/9/73	4/19/73	Production	Miramar (VF124)
26	25	158625	4/3/73	4/24/73	Production	Miramar (VF124)
27	26	158626	4/14/73	5/2/73	Production	Miramar (VF124)
28	27	158627	5/12/73	6/5/73	Production	Miramar (VF124)

F-14A FIRST FLIGHTS AND DELIVERY (DD-250) DATES (CONT)

A/C No.	Delivered to Date	Buro No.	First Flight	DD-250	R&D Mission or Production		Location
29	28	158628	5/11/73	7/7/73	Production	●	Miramar (VF124)
30	29	158629	5/29/73	6/27/73	Production	●	Miramar (VF124)
32	30	158631	7/12/73	8/20/73	Production	●	Miramar (VF-124)
33	31	158632	7/13/73	8/28/73	Production	●	Miramar (VF-124)
34	32	158633	7/25/73	8/31/73	Production	●	Miramar (VF-124)
35	33	158634	8/21/73	9/14/73	Production	●	Miramar (VF-124)
7B	34	157986	9/12/73	9/19/73	F401 Demo	●	Calverton
36	38	158635	9/14/73	10/15/73	Production	●	Norfolk-Retrofix
37	36	158636	9/16/73	10/13/73	Production	●	Norfolk-Retrofix
38	35	158637	9/16/73	10/12/73	Production	●	Miramar (VF-124)
39	37	158978	9/21/73	10/14/73	Production	●	NMC (VX4)
40	39	158979	10/15/73	10/31/73	Production	●	Miramar CVA-1
41	40	158980	10/30/73	11/13/73	Production	●	Miramar CVA-1
42	44	158981	11/1/73	11/30/73	Production	●	Miramar CVA-1
43	45	158982	11/8/73	12/11/73	—		—
44	41	158983	11/6/73	11/23/73	Production	●	Miramar CVA-1
45	42	158984	11/10/73	11/28/73	Production	●	Miramar CVA-1
46	46	158985	11/20/73	12/17/73	Production	●	Miramar CVA-1
47	43	158986	11/10/73	11/30/73	Production	●	Miramar CVA-1
48	50	158987	11/17/73	12/21/73	Production	●	Miramar CVA-1
49	48	158988	11/29/73	12/18/73	Production	●	Miramar CVA-1
50	51	158989	12/1/73	12/21/73	Production	●	Miramar CVA-1
51	47	158990	11/22/73	12/17/73	Production	●	Miramar CVA-1
52	52	158991	11/30/73	12/21/73	Production	●	Miramar CVA-1
53	53	158992	12/3/73	12/21/73	Production	●	Miramar CVA-1
54	49	158993	12/2/73	12/20/73	Production	●	Miramar CVA-1
55	58	158994	12/12/73	2/21/74	Production	●	Miramar CVA-1
56	54	158995	12/14/73	1/30/74	Production	●	Miramar CVA-1
57	55	158996	12/18/73	2/12/74	Production	●	Miramar CVA-1

A/C No.	Delivered To Date	Buro No.	First Flight	DD250	R&D Mission or Production	Location
58	56	158997	12/20/73	2/15/74	● Production	Miramar CVA-1
59	57	158998	1/12/74	2/20/74	● Production	Miramar CVA-1
60	59	158999	1/25/74	3/12/74	● Production	Miramar CVA-1
61	61	159000	1/24/74	3/18/74	● Production	Miramar CVA-1
62	60	159001	2/5/74	3/14/74	● —	—
63	62	159002	2/6/74	3/18/74	● Production	Miramar CVA-1
64	71	159003	2/20/74	4/25/74	● Production	Miramar CVA-1
65	72	159004	3/5/74	4/26/74	● Production	Miramar CVA-1
66	65	159005	9/10/74	12/6/74	● Production	Pt. Mugu (UP-2)
67	67	159006	2/24/74	4/15/74	● Production	Miramar (VF-124)
68	64	159007	3/14/74	3/22/74	● Production	Oceana (VF-14)
69	63	159008	3/5/74	3/18/74	● Production	Oceana (VF-32)
70	66	159009	3/19/74	4/5/74	● Production	Oceana (VF-32)
71	68	159010	3/26/74	4/19/74	● Production	Oceana (VF-32)
72	70	159011	4/6/74	4/24/74	● Production	Oceana (VF-14)
73	69	159012	4/1/74	4/19/74	● Production	Oceana (VF-14)
74	73	159013	4/6/74	5/17/74	● Production	Oceana (VF-32)
75	75	159014	4/24/74	5/28/74	● Production	Oceana (VF-14)
76	74	159015	4/29/74	5/22/74	● Production	Oceana (VF-32)
77	77	159016	5/7/74	6/10/74	● Production	Oceana (VF-32)
78	76	159017	5/15/74	6/8/74	● Production	Oceana (VF-14)
79	79	159018	5/16/74	6/17/74	● Production	Oceana (VF-32)
80	78	159019	5/28/74	6/11/74	● Production	Oceana (VF-14)
81	81	159020	6/3/74	7/12/74	● Production	Oceana (VF-14)
82	80	159021	6/4/74	6/30/74	● Production	Oceana (VF-32)
83	82	159022	6/10/74	7/15/74	● Production	Oceana (VF-32)
84	83	159023	6/20/74	7/19/74	● Production	Oceana (VF-14)
85	86	159024	6/18/74	8/19/74	● Production	Oceana (VF-14)
86	84	159025	6/28/74	7/31/74	● Production	Oceana (VF-32)
87	85	159421	7/19/74	8/9/74	● Production	Oceana (VF-14)
88	90	159422	7/26/74	9/19/74	● Production	Pt. Mugu (UP-2)
89	88	159423	7/22/74	9/4/74	● Production	Pt. Mugu (UP-2)

F-14A FIRST FLIGHTS AND DELIVERY (DD-250) DATES (CONT)

A/C No.	Delivered To Date	Buro No.	First Flight	DD-250	R&D Mission or Production	Location
90	87	159424	8/5/74	8/21/74	• Production	• NMC
91	93	159425	8/8/74	10/6/74	• Production	• Pt. Mugu (UP-2)
92	89	159426	8/15/74	9/18/74	• Production	• Pt. Mugu (UP-2)
93	94	159427	8/22/74	10/6/74	• Production	• Miramar (VF-124)
94	91	159428	8/25/74	10/4/74	• Production	• Miramar (VF-124)
95	92	159429	9/5/74	10/5/74	• Production	• Miramar (VF-124)
96	95	159430	9/13/74	10/7/74	• Production	• Miramar (VF-124)
97	96	159431	10/5/74	10/18/74	• Production	• Miramar (VF-124)
98	100	159432	10/1/74	11/10/74	• Production	• Miramar (VF-124)
99	99	159433	9/26/74	11/7/74	• Production	• Miramar (VF-124)
100	98	159434	10/3/74	11/5/74	• Production	• Miramar (VF-124)
101	97	159435	10/6/74	10/26/74	• Production	• Miramar (VF-124)
102	102	159436	10/12/74	11/14/74	• Production	• Miramar (VF-124)
103	103	159437	10/11/74	11/21/74	• Production	• Miramar (VF-124)
104	108	159438	10/22/74	12/9/74	• Production	• Miramar (VF-124)
105	101	159439	10/26/74	11/11/74	• Production	• Miramar (VF-124)
106	106	159440	11/15/74	12/6/74	• Production	• Miramar (VF-124)
107	104	159441	11/6/74	11/30/74	• Production	• Miramar (VF-124)
108	105	159442	11/9/74	11/30/74	• Production	• Miramar (VF-124)
109	111	159443	11/13/74	12/16/74	• Production	• Miramar (VF-124)
110	107	159444	11/24/74	12/6/74	• Production	• Miramar (VF-124)
111	110	159445	11/27/74	12/12/74	• Production	• Miramar (VF-124)
112	109	159446	12/3/74	12/11/74	• Production	• Miramar (VF-124)
113	112	159447	11/30/74	12/19/74	• Production	• Miramar (VF-124)
114	113	159448	12/5/74	12/19/74	• Production	• Miramar (VF-124)
115	114	159449	12/7/74	1/13/75	• Production	• Miramar (VF-124)
116		159450	12/11/74		• Production	• Await. Deliv.
117		159451	12/19/74		• Production	
118		159452	12/19/74		• Production	

Index

References to drawings, charts, graphs or photos are in **boldface** type. Where both illustrations and text references are within the same pages, ***boldface italics*** are used. All other numbers represent text references.

Index

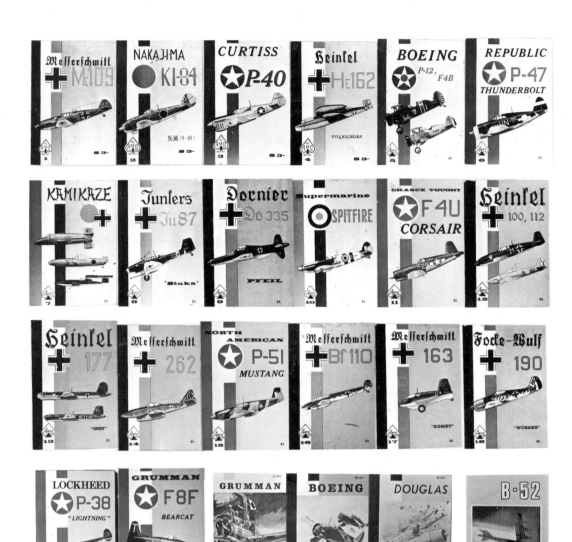

AERO SERIES

A detailed look at many of the world's most famous and noteworthy military aircraft. Each book contains historical commentary, selected photographic material covering all aspects of the aircraft, technical data and specifications, four pages of color drawings, plus much more. Provides an unprecedented source of material for the modeler, military enthusiast, collector and historian.

Volumes 1 thru 20 $3.00(A) each.